FOREVER MY HOMELAND

All My Love, Detrick
BOOK FIVE

ROBERTA KAGAN

2nd Edition

ISBN (eBook): 978-1-957207-47-6
ISBN (Paperback): 978-1-957207-48-3
ISBN (Hardcover): 978-1-957207-49-0

Title Production by The Book Whisperer

PROLOGUE

NINA AMSEL RAN AS FAST as she could, with her swollen legs and the extra weight she was not used to carrying on her small frame. With sweat-slick palms, she held tightly to her distended, pregnant belly, hoping to ease the strain on the baby huddled inside, trusting her for protection. She gagged as her heart thundered in her throat. The heaviness of her body, combined with exertion and fear, made her breath ragged and uneven.

The PLO had discovered the truth. She had no idea how they knew. Perhaps she and her husband, Elan, were the reason they took the plane hostage in the first place. However, the PLO had now made it clear that they knew that she and Elan were Mossad agents.

They had escaped together, but then two terrorists had come toward them in the darkness. She'd ducked into a dark doorway, but when she looked for Elan, he was gone. The airport in Uganda was like a maze, a dark web of passages and corridors, all looking alike but all unfamiliar. Somehow, she must find her husband in this spiderweb of hallways. If the terrorists who'd taken control of the

Airbus in France caught him before she could get to him, there was no doubt they would kill him.

The PLO hated Jews, but even more, they hated Mossad, and she and Elan were Mossad agents. Nina was hyperventilating, gasping for air. She had to stop and hold on to the side of the building to try to calm herself, at least for the sake of the baby. Her hand left a print in sweat on the wall where she held on for support.

Elan, dear God, where is Elan? She could not cry out, or they would surely find her. Breathe, breathe, she willed herself. As soon as she was able, Nina began moving again. Hugging the wall, she tiptoed quietly through the corridors, searching each room, listening in the empty blackness for voices, for sounds that would give her any indication of either danger or the presence of her beloved husband.

Her fine-tuned hearing listened while her eyes darted from side-to-side. Even the slightest movement, the smallest of sounds, registered in her mind. Still moving, going forward, she must find Elan.

Then she detected the whispers. Stopping quickly, she stood perfectly still. There was no denying it. What she had heard was the sound of voices. The terrible, threatening voices of the members of the PLO. Her throat felt like sandpaper as she approached the doorway. Hiding from their sight, she listened.

"Mossad? You son of a bitch, you are an agent with Mossad. Did you think we would let you live? You filthy Jew!"

She peeked inside. Elan was in the room. His hands and feet were bound with a thick rope to a chair. His mouth was covered with duct tape, but his eyes were defined. That was Elan. He would never back down, plead, or cry, even though there was no possible way that he could escape.

One of the terrorists was waving a machete. Did they plan to behead him? Oh God! She had heard about the beheadings. There are seven of them. She counted them twice to be sure. *Seven! I cannot fight them alone; even worse, I am unarmed and pregnant.*

Yes, they were going to behead him. She saw the man lift the machete and shove the blade in Elan's face. They wanted to make sure that he saw clearly what they had in store for him. This was the torture they wanted to inflict upon him before they allowed him to die. Nina had to do something. This man was not only her husband, but he had been her partner in Mossad, her best friend, and the father of her unborn child. Something, Nina—do something!

One of the terrorists, a skinny man barely older than a boy, stood over Elan. He whispered something, but Nina could not hear him clearly enough to understand his words. Then, he spit in Elan's face. One of the older terrorists, this one, a man perhaps twenty-five years old, took the machete from the younger man. His dark eyes glittered with anger and hatred as he held the blade high. The light reflected in the steel as it slid through the air. When the knife had almost made contact with Elan's neck, Nina awakened.

She found herself in her home, in her bed beside Elan, but she was sitting up and screaming. He'd awakened, too, and was holding her in his arms. These dreams had been reoccurring since they had escaped from the terrorists holding the Jews hostage in Uganda. Nina and Elan had been returning from a vacation in Paris when the PLO hijacked and diverted the plane to Uganda.

It was a terrifying experience, but it all worked out very well in the end. The IDF had planned and executed a marvelous escape. Although Nina and Elan had been involved in dangerous missions before, she was now pregnant. That very fact changed the way she looked at everything.

When she was younger, she'd looked at her Mossad missions as adventures, but now she saw them as the life-threatening terrors that they were. This pregnancy had not come to her easily. She'd had a difficult time conceiving. She'd prayed every day for five years to be blessed with a child. Now that she was pregnant, she and Elan wanted to protect this new life in every way possible.

Once the escape was over and they returned safely to Israel, she and Elan retired from Mossad. That had been a difficult decision because Mossad was a job to which both had dedicated their lives.

Nina's slender body was convulsing.

"Shhhh, you're all right. You're here at home. You're safe in my arms," Elan said.

Nina tried to calm herself. She leaned her head on his muscular chest. Although he was twenty years her senior, he still had the strongest and tightest body of any man she'd ever known.

Elan rocked his wife in his arms like a baby. He was the only person who had ever seen his wife's vulnerability. It had taken her a long time to let him get that close to her.

"Nina, Nina," he whispered, almost like a song into her long, curly dark hair.

"It was the dream again," she said, her voice hoarse.

"I know," he whispered, "but it was only a nightmare. It never even happened that way. I was never exposed as a Mossad agent at Entebbe. We were just Israeli captives, as far as they knew. You are safe with me in our home, our bed, and this quiet little village. We're just far enough outside of Tel Aviv to avoid the crowds but close enough for us to go into the city for a good meal, yes?" he asked, trying to make her laugh at least a little.

She nodded her head.

"Speaking of a good meal…" He tried to make his voice casual. But of course, he knew she still remembered the narrow escape from Entebbe. He understood because he could not forget the escape and how he'd felt as he looked back through the window of the jeep that the IDF had loaded them into and saw the body of their dear friend Yoni Netanyahu lying dead, his blood pooling on the concrete. "Maybe," Elan cleared his throat, "we should go into the city tomorrow night and have a nice dinner?"

"We'll see. I hate to leave here."

It was hard to believe that once his Nina had been a special agent with Mossad. Together, they'd taken unfathomable risks. He wondered if all women got this way when they became pregnant. Perhaps their hormones made them jittery, on edge, and nervous. In a way, although he would never tell her, Elan loved Nina this way. She had been so independent before, and he'd been crazy with desire for that independent girl. But now, he felt like a lion, her protector. No matter what the future brought, Elan decided he would not fail this woman, who continually captured and recaptured his heart.

"Do you want some water?" he whispered into her hair.

"No."

"Ahhh, how about some figs? Did you know I brought you a bunch of dried figs when I went to the market yesterday?"

She laughed a little. Sometimes, Elan could be especially thoughtful. He knew how much she'd come to love anything sweet since getting pregnant. "Yes, maybe some figs."

He stretched out his long legs and stood up. In his white briefs, his muscular tan legs looked like the legs of an Olympian. Elan knew that he owed his well-honed body to years of discipline. He'd started a daily routine of running, weightlifting, sit-ups, and push-ups when he first served as a young man in the IDF, and he liked the way exercise made him feel. In fact, after a full hour and a half of strenuous workout, he had a feeling of euphoria. So, he'd continued the routine throughout his life. "You stay here. I'll be right back," Elan said as he leaned over and kissed Nina's head.

Elan put several figs on a small plate and poured a glass of water. Nina. She was so young and beautiful. Every time he looked at her, he found it hard to believe that such a woman would choose to marry a man twenty years her senior. Whenever they went anywhere, he watched the faces of the younger men as they stared at him with envy. He had to admit he enjoyed the feeling, but at the same time, it threatened him. He wondered if she would lose her attraction to him and find another man when he grew older. The very idea sent a chill of insecurity down his spine, and Elan Amsel had never before been insecure in his life.

"Here you go, sweetheart," he said, placing the plate on her lap and the water glass on the small table next to the bed. Then, he went to the bathroom and got a wet washcloth. Gently, he patted the sweat off of her face.

"I cannot believe how nervous and sensitive I've become. Suddenly, I am going to be a mother, and now everything bothers me…"

"I know, I know. It's all right. Soon, you'll have the baby, and you'll feel much better. Your hormones will get back to normal."

"I suppose everything is just going so well, you know? It makes me afraid to lose the wonderful things I have. That makes no sense, I know."

"It does. It makes all the sense in the world. As much as I miss working with Mossad and all the excitement, I feel that I would not want to put myself at risk because, finally, someone loves me and really needs me."

"Elan. I do love you. Thank you for trying to understand me, even when I don't understand myself." She kissed him, and the figs spilled on the blanket. He pushed the blanket out of his way and took her into his arms. She melted into him, into his strength. Nina let herself be lost in the security of Elan's strong body. Then, gently, slowly, and carefully, he made love to her.

CHAPTER ONE

THE BABY WAS due in early spring, but by the middle of January, Nina was huge. Meat, vegetables, fruit, and milk tasted strange to her. She could not bear to eat healthy food, only sweets, and she'd gained eighty pounds. That was a lot of weight on her small frame. Her ankles and legs began to swell. Her breasts were large, tender, and uncomfortable. The wedding ring she wore had to be cut off in the emergency room at the local hospital because it was digging so deep into her swollen finger that it became painful.

But more importantly, her mind was not stable. Most of the time, Nina was fearful, sometimes edgy and agitated, other times quiet and almost comatose. She would catch imaginary glimpses of the people she'd been forced to execute during her missions in Mossad. Intellectually, she knew that these visions were not real. These people were dead, but sometimes, she would see someone moving in the corner of her vision.

One morning, she was boiling water for tea when she heard a noise outside the kitchen window. She glanced out but saw nothing. Then, in her peripheral vision, she caught a quick glimpse of one of the men who she'd shot when she was involved with Operation Wrath of God. The ghost was gone as quickly as he appeared.

But then she noticed that the branches of the olive tree in her front yard had come alive and were reaching in desperation for heaven, their silver leaves trembling with fear. She became so frightened that she accidentally knocked the glass cup off the countertop and into the sink. It broke into shards that looked like icicles. Nina began to clean the mess, but the glass felt cold. For a minute, she thought that perhaps it was ice and not glass at all. Could she possibly have imagined breaking a glass?

Nina looked out at the tree again. It was no longer alive. Everything was as it should be. Was all of this a dream, but she was awake? What was happening to her? Elan had heard the glass breaking and came into the kitchen, where he found her with her hands bleeding. He looked at her with such concern that she thought she might cry. Then Elan took her bloody hands into his own, brought them to his lips, and kissed them.

He escorted her out of the kitchen and sat her down on the sofa in the living room. "I'll be right back—stay right here," he whispered to her. Then, he got the first aid kit they kept in the bathroom and gently cleaned her wounds. She sat quietly and stared at him.

When he finished, he did not speak but took her into his arms and held her until the pot of water she'd left in the kitchen was boiling. Then he kissed the top of her head and went to make her a cup of tea.

Elan was worried. Nina did not look good. She was not glowing with health like he'd always been told that a pregnant woman should. Every night, she had trouble sleeping. Not only was her body heavy, but she had to urinate constantly through the night. Nina had constant heartburn and adamantly refused when Elan tried to convince her to eat fruit or vegetables. Her once thick, lustrous hair was now dry and frizzy. But the worst of it was that she'd seen spots of blood on her underwear. This pregnancy had not been easy to achieve. It had taken the couple five years and a trip to France for Nina to conceive. If she lost the baby, Elan knew Nina would be devastated.

But what scared him the most was that Nina had always been the type of person to stay active. Even after she'd left Mossad, she'd found things to keep her busy. She'd gardened and made curtains, but during the last few months of her pregnancy, she was too lethargic to be interested in anything. She was always tired and never felt well enough to take walks or get much exercise, even at Elan's insistence.

Since Nina slept a lot of the time, Elan was often alone. Untrue to his character, he had no interest in looking for other women. The old Elan, the womanizer, had disappeared when he fell in love with Nina. He didn't miss the wild antics of his youth, but he did secretly miss working. He enjoyed having a purpose and somewhere to go.

For Elan, there was a special camaraderie and excitement that came with being a part of an important organization, especially one that was essential to the survival of his beloved Israel. And yes, he hated to acknowledge it, but he missed the danger, that moment when he was not sure if he would come out of a mission alive. It was a strange thing to long for, but that adrenalin flow that filled his body just after he came within inches of death and survived was like nothing he could explain.

Well, he'd promised Nina that he would be done with all of that, and he was. But perhaps once the baby was born and Nina was back to herself, he would see how she felt about him going back to work with Mossad. He would not be an agent, of course, but in the office, out of immediate danger, but still a part of the agency that kept Israel safe, the Secret Service of Israel, Mossad.

Elan Amsel found it difficult to keep himself busy. He had no interest in books or building things around the house. He turned on the television, but he lost interest quickly unless a sports event was being aired. He did his best to cook for Nina, hoping that she would eat, but most of the time, his efforts failed. Elan considered getting a puppy, a dog he could train. But he was afraid that in its exuberance, the dog might jump on Nina and accidentally injure the baby. Right now, they were both being very careful. After the blood spots, Nina went to see her doctor, who prescribed staying off her feet. In fact, he insisted that she get up only to shower once a day.

By February, Nina was in her eighth month of pregnancy. She was bored and depressed with staying in all the time. She was still tired, but she felt as if life was passing her by. She constantly complained about how much she hated her stretched-out body and how sure she was that it would never be the same again. Elan shook his head. Women made no sense to him. She'd wanted to have a child more than anything else in the world, and now, he would catch her standing naked in front of the mirror and crying. And yet, when he talked to her about the baby, she was excited and happy. Women!

They still had not agreed on a name for one more month until the baby was born. Nina was lying on the bed with piles of books that contained the names of babies surrounding her. She had lists of names for boys and more for girls, but she could not decide. If Elan pushed her to make a choice, she snapped at him. So, he stopped trying to force the issue.

One morning, Nina felt as if her bladder might explode. She got out of bed and stood up to go to the bathroom. Her nightgown was covered in blood, and the sheets were soaked.

"Elan, get up!" She pushed hard on his shoulder.

He opened his eyes to see her standing over him. The white cotton of her nightdress stained with red shook him awake instantly.

"Nina. Oh my God!"

He was immediately on his feet. Taking her arm, he led her to a chair in the living room. "Stay here. I'll call the doctor."

The doctor told Elan to call an ambulance, and he would meet them at the hospital in Tel Aviv.

Elan was usually calm in a crisis. He'd been close to death more times than he could remember. But seeing his young wife sitting on the living room chair, her face whiter than their bedroom sheets and a pool of blood beginning to form at her feet, unnerved him. It seemed to Elan that the ambulance was taking too long. He would give them another five minutes, and then he would take control and drive Nina to the hospital.

He knelt at Nina's side and held her hand in both hands. Elan was no stranger to death, and because of what he'd seen, he knew that Nina was losing too much blood. At first, his worries had been for the baby, but now, as he saw her condition worsening, all he could think of was losing her. He'd endured the death of those he loved before, and it hurt, but he'd never felt such panic and even guilt. After all, even though she wanted a child, it was his sperm that made her pregnant. So, the responsibility for whatever happened to her fell upon him.

The paramedics finally arrived. Elan helplessly watched as they lay Nina's small frame with her large belly on a stretcher. One of her tiny feet stuck out of the blanket, and just seeing her small toenails painted pink against her olive skin made him want to cry.

He followed the group into the ambulance and sat beside her, holding tightly to her hand as if he could somehow transmit his strength through his grasp into her. Elan would gladly have traded places with Nina. But of course, Elan knew better than to bargain with God. He'd tried that in the past, and he'd never been successful. God had never listened to him.

The loud roaring of the ambulance siren blared in his ears as Elan thought of all the men he'd killed in battle and all the people he'd killed with Mossad. He'd never given a thought to their families until now. Watching Nina, he felt their losses. It was his job to kill when enemies threatened Israel.

He loved his country, and he understood how important the existence of Israel was to the survival of his people. He didn't regret doing his duty; if needed, he would do it again. But if there were to finally be peace, and he never had to kill another person, he would gladly do it. Death had an ugly face, and to Elan Amsel, death was no stranger.

Nina's hand was growing cold in his. He knew what that meant. He prayed. Even though he didn't believe in God, he still prayed. There was nothing to do but pray. "God, if you are real as the rabbis claim that you are, and if you are there listening, I am pleading with you to have mercy upon her. I am not worthy of your forgiveness, but she is just a girl. She is so young. Please, God, I am begging you. Please..." Her lips were cracked and covered with a white film. She tried to speak, but her voice was so soft he could not hear it over the cry of the ambulance horn. He bent his head to her lips but still could not hear her.

When they arrived at the hospital, Elan was pushed out of the way as Nina was rolled into surgery. As the stretcher seemed to fly down the hall, Elan's eyes caught Nina's. She smiled at him. She looked unafraid. He began to cry and weep as he'd never wept before. He fell against the wall and buckled over at the waist. Holding his face in his hands, Elan Amsel wept.

He knew this would be the last time he saw his beautiful wife alive. Several hours passed before the doctor came out to tell him what he already knew. His wife was dead. Elan Amsel was a widower and was all alone in the world. Alone, even though his child was alive. He had a daughter. Elan could not look at the child. He refused. Instead, he telephoned his brother Aryeh and told him about the situation. If Aryeh and his wife, Brenda, did not come to take the baby, Elan would put the little girl up for adoption. His only feelings toward the infant right now were anger and hatred.

Aryeh and Brenda arrived at the hospital a few hours later. Elan signed the papers over to them. They named the little girl Noa for her mother, Nina, and then took the baby home. Elan never once peeked into the blanket to see his child. Brenda carried the baby, and Aryeh followed behind her. They turned the corner at the end of the corridor, leaving Elan standing alone in the hall of the hospital. His golden, sun-kissed skin looked alien against the antiseptic white walls.

CHAPTER TWO

THE DAY NINA DIED, Elan lost the will to live. What was the point of going on? Yes, he loved Israel. He'd been willing to fight for and die for her, but he was no longer the same man he was before he'd met his precious Nina.

Like a tender plant rising from the earth, slowly, she'd shown him that the love of a woman could engulf him in an embrace so strong that he would lose all sense of reason. With her bright smile and deep understanding of his very essence, she had seeped into the marrow of his bones. Then slowly, ever so slowly, so that he didn't even realize what was happening, she'd become his entire world.

Once, long ago, before he met Nina, he had loved a woman, Katja, but he'd given her up because of his foolish pride. She was not born Jewish. In his youth and arrogance, he was too self-right-eous to go forward with their marriage, so he broke off the engage-ment. It had hurt him more deeply than he could ever admit to anyone. He had loved her, but not the way he loved Nina.

Nina brought emotions to the surface that lay deep inside Elan, emotions he had never known he could feel. Maybe it was because she was so much younger than him and so beautiful that he felt in awe that she could even care for him.

After Katja, he knew he had to go forward with his life. So, he'd made the foolish mistake of marrying an American girl he had not loved. Her name was Janice, and he did her a great disservice. Elan still felt guilty about dragging her into his life just to help him get over Katja.

The relationship between Elan and Janice was a pure disaster. They were two strong-willed people constantly at odds with each other. There were no tender feelings on Elan's part to buffer their constant arguments. He was relieved when she'd finally left him to return home to her parents.

At that point, Elan was sure he was done with serious relationships with women. He still had *needs*, but that was all they were: physical needs, like the need to eat, sleep, or even urinate. To satisfy those urges, he had passionate but short-term affairs or one-night stands that meant little more to him than a quick game of tennis. Strangely enough, Elan thought he was satisfied with his life.

But then, by some miracle, he'd met Nina. Like a crystal pitcher, pure and sparkling, her youthful exuberance, filled with sweet wine, poured into his worn and damaged heart, filling it with a thirst for more. His heart opened wider than he thought possible, and it drank of her spirit as if it were a man parched and dying of thirst in the desert. Then, before he knew it, Elan Amsel was truly in love.

There would be no shiva, at least not at the home Elan shared with Nina. He didn't care what her parents decided to do—that didn't concern him. All Elan knew was that he could see no point in having a house full of guests right now.

Elan's brother and his brother's wife came to his house to help him dress and prepare for the funeral. They rang the doorbell, waited several minutes, and then rang again. His brother called out his name while banging on the window. Elan, frustrated and annoyed, finally opened the door, but he ordered them to leave. He would not attend the funeral. He had no desire to see his in-laws or his friends or to feel their pity. As far as Elan was concerned, he didn't deserve to be comforted. In fact, he refused to be comforted. It was his fault. He'd made her pregnant, and now he deserved to suffer.

After Aryeh and Brenda left, Elan was alone. He sat in the darkness, surrounded by a silence that was broken only occasionally by the sound of an automobile going by outside his window. He preferred the darkness. The light only made his reality more unbearable.

Oh, Nina. What am I going to do without you? Elan said aloud to the empty room. Everything in the little house he'd once shared with his late wife now had memories that tore him apart: the copper pots hanging above the stove, the extra red and white blanket folded carefully on the end of the bed, and Nina's tiny white slippers. Elan noticed a small gray stain on the front of one of the slippers, and just looking at the dark spot, he felt overwhelmed with grief.

The days passed, and Elan did not dress. He stayed in his underwear, unshaven, with his hair uncombed. In fact, he could not remember the last time he'd showered. After he had plopped himself in his recliner, he didn't leave his seat unless he had to use the bathroom.

On the table beside him, a half-full bottle of whiskey kept him company. On the floor in front of him, several empty bottles lay abandoned. This was not the first time in Elan's life when he'd buried himself in alcohol. He could not even bear to hear the sound of the television set or the radio. So, he continued to sit in silence, reliving the memories of his lost love over and over again.

Sometimes, he fell asleep sitting up with his head leaning back on the chair or slumped onto the table. Once, he'd knocked the bottle to the floor, shattering the glass. A shard had cut his leg, but it had not even awakened him. When he did awaken, he cursed at the wasted liquor, then got up and went to the kitchen, where he got another bottle.

Elan wallowed in self-pity for days and days. Once in a while, he would try to eat, but the food stuck in his throat. Even though he'd done nothing, his emotions had left him exhausted. Finally, he decided to go into the bedroom to lie down. When he pulled back the blankets, he saw the blood on the sheets and eyed a strand of Nina's hair on her pillow. He took the hair into his fingers and held it to his heart. Then, the reality set in again as vomit rose in his throat.

Nina was never coming home. His beloved wife was dead, snatched away from him, right in the prime of her life. Why had God not taken him? He was a good-for-nothing, a cad of a man with plenty of sins under his belt. So, what kind of cruel, merciless God would take a beautiful, kind, loving woman who deserved to live while leaving him to wade alone through the tumultuous waters of life? "Damn you!" he yelled at God. "I forsake you…"

Then Elan sat down, put his face in his hands, and wept.

Several weeks passed. Elan ate very little, but he began to sleep a great deal. He moved from his recliner to the sofa where he lay and let the liquor do its magic. His dreams were sometimes fulfilling. She came to him in dreams. He could see her—touch her. It was his Nina in that white lace dress she'd worn the night they went dancing, her hair loose and flowing in wild curls framing her lovely face. Elan spoke to her, "I love you, Nina…"

"I love you too, Elan," she answered him. He felt her soft, featherlike touch on his brow. The only time Elan felt at peace was when he was asleep. Sometimes, the dreams felt so real that the pain was even harsher when he awoke to reality. His eyes would open to the empty room, and his face would contort until tears covered it. Elan Amsel considered suicide because then he might sleep and never have to awaken.

But once he entertained the idea of ending his life, Nina began to haunt his dreams. She would not allow him to come to her in peace. Every time he drifted off to sleep in an alcohol-induced slumber, she would return, reminding him that he had a daughter, a fact he was trying hard to forget.

He had never even named the baby. Aryeh had called and asked him if it was all right. If they named the child Noa. She would be named for Nina. According to Jewish custom, parents often took the first letter of the name of a dear family member who had died and used it to name the child. It didn't matter to Elan. But that baby had meant the world to Nina. She began scolding him in his dreams, forcing him to face the fact that their little girl was his responsibility.

Whenever Nina appeared to him in a dream, she reminded him that she'd died to bring their baby into the world and how he had abandoned the child. Nina threatened to stop coming to him. She would leave him to face the emptiness alone.

Even sleep would bring him no peace if he did not go to Aryeh's house and, at least, look at the face of his newborn infant, but Elan could not bring himself to go. He had no desire to see the child who stole his beloved wife from him, this baby demon who had ruined his life and was named for his beloved Nina.

Elan began smoking again. It had been years since he'd quit, but he'd gotten into his car and driven to the store just to buy a package of cigarettes. He wanted to hurt himself, to punish himself for impregnating Nina and killing her.

Coworkers and friends who knew Elan and Nina from Mossad came to see Elan, but he would not open the door when they knocked. Sometimes, he would look through the peephole and walk away. Other times, the doorbell would ring, but Elan would not even get out of his chair to see who was there. He simply ignored them until they left.

Early one morning in May, Elan noticed that the flowers that Nina had planted outside the kitchen window of their home had begun to bloom. The beauty of the tiny buds made him angry, furious, in fact. Because he had been burying all his feelings in a bottle of whiskey, this was the first emotion he'd felt in a long time.

Elan ran outside, still in his briefs, without a shirt, and his hair was long and disheveled. In a moment of sheer rage, he tore the flower buds from the wooden box that Nina had carefully hung on the windowsill. He tore them and threw them to the ground. Then he called out to God, "Why God? Why Nina?" But there was no answer.

He fell to his knees. The concrete of the sidewalk cut his legs, but he didn't feel the sting because the pain in his heart consumed him, and he could feel nothing else. As he looked up at the sky, Elan began to weep. His grief blinded him, so he didn't notice Brenda, his brother's wife, walking toward him carrying a small bundle. She came up and sat beside him.

"Hi, Elan," she said. "I've been coming every day, but you haven't answered the door." Her voice was soft.

Elan got up and headed inside. He wanted to close the door in her face and force her to leave him alone, but Brenda followed him, stopped the door with her foot, and entered behind him. Elan glared at her.

"What the hell do you want?"

"This is your daughter, Noa," Brenda said. "I thought you should see her."

"I don't want to see her. I have no desire to ever see her."

"That's too bad. She's here, and I'm not leaving until you look at her."

Brenda unwrapped the small bundle, removing the blanket. Surprisingly, the baby slept peacefully, her tiny fists clenched as her chest rose and fell with each breath. Elan turned away.

"Look, Elan, look at her. She is alive. Look, if you would just take a second, you will see how much she looks like Nina."

"Get her out of here…"

"She has Nina's eyes…"

Elan could not help himself. He glanced at the infant who had just awakened. Noa had dark, almond-shaped eyes like her mother.

"And her nose, too. She looks so much like Nina."

It was true. She did. Noa looked like a tiny version of her mother. It was almost as if Nina were reborn. Elan surprised himself. A million emotions rushed over him, and he reached for the baby. Miraculously, Noa didn't cry when Elan took her into his arms, but Elan did. He sobbed. His tears fell across his cheeks. He rocked his child in his arms as he wept for the beauty and joy of the small flicker of light that looked up at him with Nina's eyes. Elan held the baby to his chest. He felt the small heart beating against his. Nina, he whispered in his mind. Nina, you were right. Then, Elan looked around the room for the first time in months. It was a disaster.

"Thank you, Brenda," he said, his voice barely audible.

Brenda smiled at him. "She's a beautiful baby, Elan. Nina would have been so happy."

"Will you take her home with you and bring her back tomorrow? I'll need the night to clean this place, and then I'll have to go into town to get what I need to set up the nursery. This is her home, here with me and the memory of her mother."

"I know you didn't buy anything for a nursery because of the superstitions. Would you like me to have Aryeh come by tonight and bring a crib and other things?"

Elan nodded, hanging his head. He was spent. "Yes. Please bring what you have." It was hard for him, but he was trying to show his gratitude. His anger at God and the world was fading. "Thank you again, especially for your persistence."

That night, Aryeh brought a crib, a playpen, and several other items Elan would need for his daughter. Elan could not bring himself to speak much to his brother. His emotions were too close to the surface, and it had always been hard for Elan Amsel to show weakness in front of Aryeh.

"Brenda will bring Noa in the morning," Aryeh said.

Elan nodded.

After Aryeh left, Elan took a shower, shaved, and stared out the window. He had no experience with babies. How was he going to care for this child? He took the phone book from the cabinet and looked up home care nursing services. There were several, but only one specialized in the care of infants. He left the book open to the page and decided that he would call them first thing in the morning and went to bed. Surprisingly, he fell asleep quickly and awakened with a smile. He'd had a dream of Nina that was so real that it was hard to believe that his wife was not lying on the bed beside him. She told him how happy she was that he would raise Noa. She would be with him always, in spirit, she said. He felt an inner calm, a peaceful feeling he'd not felt since Nina died. Elan would manage. He would do his best to be a good father; wherever Nina was, she would be proud.

CHAPTER THREE

GLORIA FINKELSTEIN WAS NOT A TRAINED nurse by trade, but she
had been a mother of two children, a boy and a girl. The day Elan
hired her through the agency, she moved into the nursery in the
Amsel home. Gloria was a survivor of the Holocaust who had been
in several concentration camps and was the only one in her family
who was still alive. Once the camps were liberated, Gloria searched
for friends and family, only to find that she was alone.

When Israel became a nation, she'd gotten onto a boat and
migrated to the Jewish homeland without any possessions or loved
ones. Kibbutz life was too invasive for her: too many people. After
the crowded camps, the disease, and the horrors, Gloria had
become a private person. It was hard for her to talk about her
family or past, and she didn't want to hear about the horrors others
had endured.

All she wanted to do was escape the memories. The only thing
she knew well was how to care for a home and children, so she
became a full-time, live-in housekeeper and nanny.

She'd worked for another family before she met the Amsels, a
husband and wife who were both doctors. She'd raised their three
boys until they were in high school and no longer needed a nanny.

By the time she met Elan and Noa, Gloria was well into her late fifties, but she was a remarkably strong and capable person. She was a quiet woman who, most importantly, knew when to keep her mouth shut. For that reason alone, Elan liked her right away. She was efficient but gentle with Noa and never argued with Elan's decisions. The situation was a good one for both the employer and the employee. Gloria had a place to live and a family to care for, while Elan got the help he could rely on to raise an infant.

The year that followed was a difficult one for Elan. With continuous effort and tremendous self-control, he finally managed to stop drinking in excess. Although he'd been told that he must give up his alcohol use entirely, Elan knew that he never would. He loved the feeling of the burning liquid rushing down his throat, soothing and taking the edge off the constant thoughts that plagued his ever-active mind. Since Noa came to live with Elan, he no longer thought about suicide, even though he was still terribly lonely.

Nina's memory was never far away. He could not bring himself to clean out her closet or her drawers. Her personal items were everywhere. Tiny things, like a pressed flower that fell out of the phone book or the small embroidered handkerchief her grandmother had given her, still lay on the table beside her bed.

It had been months since she passed, and Elan still had not washed Nina's pillowcase. There was no denying it. Nina had left a mark in every room in the house. Just a glimpse of her perfume bottle in the bathroom could set Elan back for the day.

Gloria was a tremendous help with Noa. She never let the baby cry long enough to awaken Elan at night. She knew her boss, Mr. Amsel, suffered from deep depression. For Elan to heal and truly become whole, he needed something to do, perhaps a job. She would wait until the right time and gently urge him to find work. Then, once he began working, Gloria would carefully ask Elan to allow her to remove all of Nina's possessions and free him of the past.

CHAPTER FOUR

THE OUTSKIRTS OF TEL AVIV; MARCH 1978

NOA WAS PLAYING on a blanket on the floor. Elan loved to watch her play. She was so intense with her toys. He could spend hours eating up her smiles and marveling at her tiny hands and feet. Elan had come to love his daughter. Elan saw more bits of Nina in her every day as Noa grew.

A cartoon was playing on the television when the phone rang. Since few people called him anymore, Elan assumed it was his brother. He stretched his back, then his arms over his head, and went into the kitchen to answer the call. Before he left Noa alone, Elan called Gloria Finkelstein, who had gone to her room to get something.

"Mrs. Finkelstein, please come out and keep an eye on Noa."

"Yes, sir," Gloria said. She was already on her way to the living room, where the baby was playing.

Elan picked up the heavy black receiver and said, "Hello."

"Amsel?"

"Yeah?" He recognized an old familiar voice, a friend from Mossad.

"It's Chi."

"How are you?"

"I'm all right. How are you?"

"I'm getting along," Elan said.

"I didn't call to make small talk. Earlier today, an eighteen-year-old girl and eleven members of the Fatah killed an American tourist. Then, they hijacked a bus that was on its way from Haifa to Tel Aviv. Close to forty people, forty Israelis, Elan, forty of our own people, were killed. Some of them were kids. We have almost eighty wounded in the hospital. Come back to Mossad, Elan. We need you... Israel needs you."

Elan put his hand on his forehead. It had been a while since he'd felt that old familiar power, that driving force that ran through his blood and pushed him to defend the country he loved. But as he thought about what Chi had just told him, what the Fatah had done to his people, he remembered what it meant to be an Israeli.

Standing in the kitchen and looking into the living room at Noa as she played on the floor, Elan was reminded that without Israel, his child and every other Jewish child had an uncertain future. Anything could happen to the Jews without Israel behind them, even another Hitler. As Elan contemplated all of this, he felt the strength and the urge to stand up and defend the land he loved seeping back into him.

"I'll be at the office in an hour," Elan said.

"I knew you would come through for us, Elan. We'll be waiting for you."

When Elan entered the offices of Mossad, he was overcome with a mixture of emotions. It was here that he first met Nina. He could still see her slender form standing in the office kitchen making coffee, but there was more than just the memory of his beloved wife here.

As he looked around the familiar room, he saw the faces of his old friends. They were the faces of his brothers and sisters. These people, like Elan, were true Israelis. The other members of Mossad came up one by one and embraced Elan, welcoming him back to his rightful place in the world. Elan Amsel was home. He didn't want to cry in front of his friends, but his eyes filled with tears.

And so began the operation "Avi Hachochma." Israel was determined to push the Fatah, allied with the South Lebanese Army, away from her border. Israel placed over thirty thousand IDF soldiers in the area south of the Litani River with shoulder-launched, rocket-propelled cluster bombs provided by the United States. Over the seven days of intense fighting, the IDF had killed at least six hundred terrorists, but two thousand civilians were massacred.

President Carter of the United States of America said that Israel was using the bombs America gave her illegally: the agreement had been for defense only. Carter threatened to cut off all military aid to Israel if they continued to use the cluster bombs. Prime Minister Begin of Israel could not risk losing America's support, so he agreed to end the war.

But for Elan, this conflict with the Fatah had different consequences. It brought him back to life. It brought him home, home to Mossad. He was older now, and he would no longer take assignments in the field. He could not risk his life because he knew that Noa needed him. He was her only living parent.

However, his extensive knowledge would be a great help at the office. Elan Amsel had worked as an undercover Mossad agent in Operation Wrath of God. When he was younger, he had served several terms in the IDF, where he'd flown bomber planes. When called up again, he'd gladly come forth for Israel and fought in the Six-Day War. Here, amongst his people, Elan was a hero. He'd devoted his life to the survival of his beloved land.

One night, several weeks after Elan's return to his position at the offices of Mossad, he returned home from work. Mrs. Finkelstein had bathed Noa and put her to bed. Then she'd left food for Elan and quietly slipped off to bed.

He took the napkin off the plate Mrs. Finkelstein had left for him and grabbed a thick piece of pita, dipping it into the fresh hummus. It was good. Gloria Finkelstein proved to be an excellent cook. The house was quiet, and Elan had a feeling of stability. After pouring a small glass of brandy, he sat down in his thick, easy chair without turning on the light in the living room. The only light came from the kitchen and filtered through the window from the full moon.

"Nina," he whispered softly into the night to not awaken the baby or Mrs. Finkelstein. "I'm trying, Nina. God knows I'm really trying. It won't be easy for a man like me to take care of a little girl, especially as she gets older. I have to admit, I don't know too much about girls.

"But I'll be damned if she doesn't look just like you. When I look at Noa, I see you, Nina. You're still here, you're still alive, and you live in our child. Her smile is your smile; that look she gets on her face when she is stubbornly resisting something, that too, is yours. Yes, love, I can still remember that look. I still remember everything, Nina, everything about you. Help me to be a good father. Guide me from wherever you are. I know. I've always hated to admit that I needed anyone else. But I need you, Nina. I've always needed you. And I'll never stop loving you, Nina, never..."

CHAPTER FIVE

Katja Zaltstein sat on a bench feeding the pigeons. When things troubled her, she often went to the park to be alone and think.

A few months ago, something terrible happened to her daughter, Ima, and she refused to tell her mother or grandmother. When Katja pressed her daughter for answers, Ima closed her out and refused to discuss the matter.

Katja's mother, Zofia, said the best thing to do was to let Ima come to them when she was ready to talk. Zofia felt that if they kept trying to force Ima to tell them what happened, Ima would only retreat further away. Katja could not help but feel lost and helpless.

She'd stopped at a bakery on her way to the park and purchased several slices of pita bread, which she now mindlessly tore into small pieces. The birds surrounded her, but she hardly noticed. It was as if she were acting on autopilot.

Katja always missed her husband, Mendel, who died fighting in the Six-Day War, but now she missed him even more. She needed his wisdom. Mendel was smart. He would have known what to do to reach Ima. *My God. My baby has been damaged, and I am so afraid that I will lose her forever.*

She poured the torn pieces of bread onto the ground. Birds came from the sky to join those that were already eating. Katja thought, no matter how much I bring, there are always more birds than bread. She was well inside the park, and there was not another bench for a half mile.

The sun peeked through the branches of the trees, and she noticed the sun as it glittered on the silver leaves of an olive tree a few feet in front of her.

"Mind if I sit here for a couple of minutes?"

Katja was startled out of her daze. A man stood in front of her. The sun was so bright behind him that it temporarily blinded her.

"Yes, of course," she said. Katja hated to disappoint anyone, even someone she didn't know.

Once the man sat down, Katja could see that he was a light-skinned black man.

"Hi," he said. "I'm John."

"Hi," Katja said.

"This is a beautiful park. In fact, all of Israel is quite beautiful," he said.

"Yes, it is. Are you visiting?"

"Yes."

"Oh, how nice! Where are you from?"

"England," he said, "but I was born and raised in America."

"Oh? America? Where?"

"New York—in Harlem."

"Is that in the City of New York or in a suburb?" Katja asked.

"It's in Manhattan. But, well, it's a rather nasty part of the city. I'm afraid it's not a good place to grow up."

"Oh?"

"Yes, it's a poverty-stricken area. Most of the people who live there are dark-skinned like me. The world is not as kind to dark-skinned people, especially men. So I studied hard, and when the time came for me to go to college, I got a scholarship to go to

England and attend a university. My goodness," he laughed. "There are so many pigeons here."

Katja laughed, "I guess I have to say that the invasion of the birds in this part of the park is my fault. I feed them, and they gather in clusters like this, waiting and hoping for more. No matter how much bread I bring, there are always too many birds. Look over there." She pointed. "You see, other types of birds are also coming. Somehow, they know when someone is feeding them. Maybe they send messages to each other like, 'We have a sucker over here with lots of bread.'" She shook her head and smiled.

He laughed.

"Where in England did you go to school?" It was good to have someone to talk to, something to distract her from her worries.

He smiled broadly, and Katja could not help but think he was a very attractive man. "Oxford."

"Oh, impressive! That is quite an accomplishment."

"For a black man, you mean?"

"I didn't say that, John. I said it was an accomplishment, and it's quite an achievement, whether you are black or white."

"I'm sorry. That was rude."

"It's all right." She shrugged. "I've heard a lot about Oxford. It's very old and established."

"Yes, that it is, and I was lucky. Even with all the progress that civil rights have made, I was still one of the few blacks in my class. I suppose I must have filled a quota." He laughed a sad and bitter laugh.

She had never met anyone like him. In fact, he was the first black man she'd ever had a conversation with. Before this, Katja had not given much thought to the Ethiopian Jews she saw walking through the streets. But now she was starting to understand that life for people with black skin was in many ways the same as life for Jews. Strangers instantly hated them for no reason at all. "What did you study?"

"Law."

"My husband was a lawyer."

"You're married?"

"I was. My husband died in the Six-Day War."

"I'm sorry," he said.

"So am I. A day doesn't go by that I don't think of him. He was my best friend. We were children together."

John nodded. "It must be hard. Do you have any kids?"

"I have a daughter. What about you? Are you married?"

"No, I've been too busy with school. Haven't had time for a relationship. Like I said before, and I hate to keep repeating myself, but it really is so much harder for a black man. My grades had to be better than the rich white boys, or I would have been thrown out of Oxford. I didn't have any family that were alumni to send money if I screwed up. So, I focused all my time and attention on studying.

"Then, I had to find a job once I finished and passed the bar. Again, race stood in the way, but I kept fighting, climbing uphill. And I've managed. I have a good job now with a good firm in England. Of course, once again, and it's to be expected, I guess... I'm the token black man. I'm here in Israel on business for my firm. Nobody else wanted to come. They thought it was too dangerous," he laughed, "so they sent the black guy."

She didn't know what to say. He was making jokes, but she could tell that beneath the humor was pain. "How long will you be staying?" Katja asked.

"A year, maybe? Maybe a little more or less. Depends on how this case goes."

Katja noticed that the birds had left. The bread was gone. A beautiful gold and black butterfly lit on a dandelion just in front of the bench where they sat. She understood this black man because Katja knew what it was like to be different.

She'd spent her life trying to fit in. Her secret was easier to hide than his. Listening to him speak made it easy for her to empathize with him. The color of his skin was right there for all the world to see.

She had kept hers well hidden, but it was always a dark reality in her heart. Katja was born to a pure Aryan mother and an SS officer. She had been genetically engineered by the Nazis and born in

Hitler's home for the Lebensborn. She was to be a perfect Aryan child.

Then, when she was very young, fortune had intervened. She'd been given to Zofia, a Jewish woman, and her husband, Isaac. They had loved and nurtured Katja and raised her as a Jew. Katja loved them and had always been grateful.

She has carried the burden of shame since discovering the truth about her birth parents. She was shamed by what the Nazis had done to her beloved adopted people. For years, she believed she was their blood. It was ironic. She was the result of an Aryan breeding program and raised by Jews. "I understand how hard it is to be different. I mean, not to fit in, not really," she said.

"Do you? I don't know if you could…"

"Believe me, I do," she said, clearing her throat. "Much more than you know."

They sat quietly side-by-side on the bench, looking out at the beauty of Israel. Israel, the land Katja had come to love—Israel, the only country she could ever call home.

"My father was Jewish," he said, "white and Jewish. My mother was black."

She didn't say anything. And again, for a long time, there was silence.

"She was working as the maid in my father's house. He was the eldest son of a big business tycoon in Manhattan's garment district. She lived in her employer's house, but her family was in Harlem. On the weekends, she would go home to see them and then return.
"

She didn't know much about America. She knew nothing about the garment district or life in New York, but she sat quietly and listened, not wanting to interrupt him.

"My mom was young and very pretty. She was only eighteen. My father was just turning twenty-one. I guess he was quite taken with her, and one thing led to another. When she became pregnant, my father's parents panicked—my white grandparents, whom I never met. His parents fired her. Then, they sent my father away to school in Boston. He never came back to see my mom. In fact, she raised me alone with the help of her parents.

"Then years later, I guess guilt kicked in, and Dad came looking for my mom. Well, he found her. He was already married and had a family. My dad came to our small apartment. My mother's father had passed away from a stroke a few years prior, so it was just my mom, her mother, and me.

"When I first saw him with his white skin, it was hard for me to believe that the man who was standing in our little living room was my father. My mom turned pale when she saw him. Her hands trembled slightly.

"I could see she was still hurt by what happened, but she didn't tell him. It was just that I knew her so well that I could read her emotions on her face. The crazy thing is, even after everything that he did, I think she still loved him.

"I was in my early teens and full of testosterone. To me, he was nothing but a stranger who'd abandoned us. I wanted to kill him. In fact, when he was trying to offer me his friendship, I punched him and bloodied his nose. My mother was furious. My gram didn't say anything.

"My father just stood there with the blood running down his face. He never raised a hand to hit me back. I'm sure it was because he knew he had wronged us in many ways. I'm sure he could see by our home just how poor we were, and he had to know how hard it was for my mother to raise a child without any financial help." John shook his head.

"When I was growing up, my mother never talked about my father. When I asked, she avoided the subject. This was the first time I learned anything about him. His name was Michael Appleman, and that afternoon, when he appeared at our apartment, was the first time I'd ever heard his name.

"From that day on, my mother got a check from him every month. I begged her not to cash it or accept anything from him, but she did. I was young and proud, but she knew we needed the money. She was getting older, and the hard work of cleaning houses was taking a toll on her body. So, she swallowed her pride and took what he gave us."

He turned and looked into Katja's eyes. "You know, my father never showed his face again, and I never went looking for him."

"How is your mother? Did she ever marry?"

"She passed away last year from an aneurysm. I miss her every day. She was a good mother. But no, she never married. She dated a few different guys but was too busy working and trying to do her best to raise me properly. She gave her life up for me. God, she wanted me to get out of the ghetto. She didn't want me to grow up poor and black. And you know what kills me?"

She shook her head.

"It breaks my heart that I am finally earning enough money to pay her back for everything she did for me. Now, I can take care of her, but she's gone. Gram and Gramps are gone, too. So, I guess I'm all alone in the world."

"I'm so sorry," Katja said. "I don't know what to say…"

"Nothing to say. I'm one of the lucky ones. By the sheer force of my mother's will, I went to school and got out of the ghetto."

Katja thought about the ghetto in Warsaw where her mother had been forced to stay until she'd been taken to a concentration camp, but she didn't say anything.

"I've seen some of the Ethiopian Jews that have been settling here in Israel," she said.

"Yes, and so have I. It's funny, isn't it? They are Jews but are still looked down upon because of their black skin."

"I don't understand people. There is far too much hatred in the world," Katja said, shaking her head.

"Yes, well, I had a professor once who said that as long as there are two human beings alive, there will be war and hatred."

"That's a terrible way of looking at life."

"But a truthful one," he said, shrugging his shoulders.

Then, as John sat listening, Katja began to open up and tell him about her problems. It was easier to talk to a stranger than someone she knew. This man who sat beside her on the park bench had no connection to her friends or family.

Katja told him the secret she kept so close to her heart: the truth about her birth parents. She talked about Elan, about Mendel, and a little about Ima. The anger, the guilt, the pain all poured out of her, and she cried. But once she had finished speaking, Katja felt more at ease than she had in many years.

John listened without judging. Without realizing it, he had given her the very thing she needed most.

The afternoon was growing old. The sun had turned golden as it began its descent from the sky. It had to be after four p.m. Katja knew the other women at her organization would be wondering where she'd gone.

"I have to go," she told him, regretting that she had to leave.

"It's bold of me to ask. I know, but perhaps can we meet here again?" He looked away so she could not see his eyes if she rejected him.

"Yes, I'd like that. Tomorrow? The same time?"

"I'll be here," he said, smiling.

And so Katja and John met in the park the following day and again the day after. From that day on, they only spent an hour or so together, his lunch hour and hers, but for Katja, it was a time of peace. She worked so hard to keep the secret of her birth parents from her Israeli friends at the organization, but with John, she was free to be herself.

Weeks passed. One day, she brought lunch and another day, he did. They discussed politics, religion, race, and romance. They talked about books, films, and live theater. Katja told John about Mendel and how much she had come to love him. But most of all, they talked about Ima. Katja explained what happened the day that Ima had experienced whatever the tragic event was that had changed her so drastically.

"I was at work and didn't even know that Ima was not home. When I got back to the house, I was late, so I started dinner, assuming Ima was in her room doing her homework.

"My mom, who lives with us, is older and always takes afternoon naps. I figured today was no exception, and I was right. Ima was missing for several hours. I went crazy. I called the police. You can't imagine how I felt. I was sure she was dead. I'd never felt so desperate in my entire life, and there was nothing I could do.

"I drove around but couldn't find her. I called her friends, but no one had seen her. My mother and I sat by the phone, waiting to hear something from the police, and at the same time, we were terrified that they would call and say they'd found her body.

"Then, much later that night, Ima came home. She was a wreck. Her clothes were torn, and she was filthy. I tell you, she was a mess. I tried to talk to her, but she locked herself in the bathroom. I thanked God that she had returned, but I had no idea what to do to help her. My mother said to let her be, just to wait. I lay awake all night in my room. I was so afraid that she might hurt herself.

"The next day, she came out of her room and looked like a different girl. She was so troubled, and she still is. I can see it in her eyes. Ima had always taken pride in her beautiful hair, but she had chopped all of it off in her bedroom sometime during the night. I am beside myself, John. I just don't know how to reach her."

John took Katja's hand. It was the first time they had made physical contact. She felt a strange mixture of desire, comfort, and fear. It had been a long time since she'd opened her heart, and she knew how intense the pain of love could be.

"Kat." He had come to call her Kat over the time they'd gotten to know each other. "I think she might have been raped."

"I know," Katja said. "So do I. I think that, too."

He gently squeezed her hand. She was aware of the difference in color as she looked at his hand on her own, and yet, it didn't matter. Katja squeezed back.

"My mother tells me over and over that all we can do is wait. She says that Ima will have to come to us. The more we try to force her to open up, the harder she pushes us away. I can see such terrible changes in her. My daughter was such an innocent girl, and now I can see by the way she dresses and stays out all night that she is becoming more promiscuous.

"Boys hover around our house like dogs in heat. It's horrifying. I've even found illegal drugs and large amounts of cash in her room. Oh God, John. I think she might be selling her body for money to buy drugs. And the hardest part of it all is that I feel so alone. I wish that her father was still alive. I keep thinking he would know what to do because I have no idea. All I know is that I am getting closer to losing my little girl every day.

"I pray that nothing happens to her, but, John, it's just a matter of time. With the life she is leading, she can only fall in with the wrong people and then, well, God knows what will happen."

"Have you tried to get her to go and see a professional?"

"You mean like a therapist?"

"Yes."

"I've tried. She refuses. She spends most of the time when she is at home in her room with the door closed. I knock and try to offer to take her shopping. She used to love to go shopping for clothes. Now, she doesn't even answer me. I'm so afraid I am going to lose my daughter. Anything can happen. She is taking drugs and running around with dangerous men. Anything can happen, John, anything…"

"I don't have any children, and I've never been married, so I can't say I know how you feel, but I can imagine."

"John, I believe that it is all my fault. I was a terrible mother. I was so busy putting all my time into building this organization for the wives of soldiers who perished in Israeli conflicts that I forgot about the needs of my own child.

"I thought Ima was fine. I never worried about her. In fact, I never realized that we should have been closer before all this happened. How could I do that? What was I thinking?

"You see, Mendel left me with plenty of money, but so many of the women who have lost their husbands in the wars are struggling. I wanted to help them. I believed that it was my duty to help. In a way, I felt guilty because I had so much material wealth, and so many of the others had so little.

"And then, somewhere, somehow, I forgot to spend time building an important bond with my daughter. I mean, I thought Ima was all right. I didn't realize that I wasn't being a mother to her. Then all of this happened, and she didn't feel close enough to me to open up to me. Somehow, I feel that I have lost her."

John said nothing, but he put his arm around Katja and let her lean on his chest. He felt her body rack and knew she was crying, but she made no sound.

"There is a good chance that she will get herself killed," Katja said. Then she looked up at John. "I hate to admit it to myself, but she is really in danger, and every day could be the day that she crosses the line. Between the drugs and prostitution and the strange men… Oh, John, what am I going to do?"

He patted her back and squinted his eyes against the sun. "All you can do, Kat, is love her and let her know that you are there and you will be there when she's ready to come to you."

"I just pray to God that she will come to me before it's too late."

CHAPTER SIX

ONE SUNNY AFTERNOON, when the sky was cloudless and even brighter blue than Katja's eyes, Katja and John met in the park.

"My mother is sick. She is going to be having chemo," Katja said as she laid out a blanket for the picnic she'd brought for John and herself. "I'm distraught. My mom has always been my best friend. If something happens to her, I don't know what I will do."

"When did you find out about the cancer?"

"Yesterday."

"My mom didn't even tell me she had been to a doctor. I guess she wasn't going to tell me if nothing was wrong. But now, she will need me to take her to the hospital."

"How can I help?" John asked.

"I don't know. I don't know if you can. Just be here for me to listen to all of my problems. You know, John, you've been such a wonderful friend all these months. I come to the park, and you let me unburden myself."

"I'm always here for you, Kat."

"My mom has been writing her memoirs. I haven't read them yet, but they are all about what happened to her in Poland during the Nazi occupation. They are about what happened to my father, too."

"That's a story that must be told," he said, "like the stories about the slaves who were brought to America from Africa. Those are stories that must be told, as well."

"We have a lot in common, John, and we have so many differences at the same time."

They sat, silently nibbling on the pita and hummus that Katja had brought. She took a slice of green pepper and bit into it. It was fresh and crisp, but she didn't enjoy it.

"Yesterday, on my way home from the market, I saw two Ethiopian Jewish women. I never noticed it before, but you're right. There is a lot of prejudice against them. I saw how they were treated as they tried to purchase some fruit from a peddler on the street. People stared at them. Although they had arrived at the stand first, the peddler helped another woman who came after they did, and he let them wait. It was obvious to me why he was acting that way. It was terrible."

"And you thought of me?"

She nodded. "Yes, and it hurt me to think you have been treated this way."

"I'm used to it. It's been like this for me all of my life."

"I know, John, I know. And I wish that I could do something to change the world."

After six months of chemotherapy, Zofia was doing better. The cancer was in remission, but she was thin and worn.

The treatment had been very difficult. It had taken a lot out of her, but she was alive, and for that, Katja gave thanks to God every day.

Now that she could, Zofia was even more adamant about finishing her memoirs. Katja knew that her mother wanted to get everything down on paper before she passed away. Zofia said she wanted to leave a tiny footprint on the earth, a memory of what had happened to the Jews under Hitler.

Ima was getting worse. She stayed out for days at a time without telling Zofia or Katja where she was or when she would return.

Katja could not sleep on the nights that Ima was away from home. It was difficult not to ponder all the terrible things that might happen.

Katja and John were forced to miss a few days of their meetings because of Zofia's treatments. For the most part, they met every day but Saturday because Saturday was Shabbat, and it would have been too difficult to explain to Zofia why Katja needed to leave the house. On Sunday, Katja would give Zofia the excuse that she was going to the market to escape and meet John.

CHAPTER SEVEN

IMA'S RAPIST was never found because the rape was never reported. Instead, it was a dark, festering wound that had taken on a silent life of its own, growing like a cancer inside Ima.

One morning, when Ima returned after being gone for four days, Katja came out of her room to see her daughter. Ima looked like an alley cat. Her hair was disheveled, her black eye makeup ran down her cheek, and her lipstick was smeared. After not sleeping for several nights, Katja was a nervous wreck. She grabbed Ima by the shoulders and shook her.

"Where have you been? I've been worried sick. You can't keep this up, Ima!" Katja screamed. "Listen to me. You are going to end up dead if you don't straighten up. I am beside myself. I don't know what to do with you anymore. Your grandmother is sick, and you are making it worse…"

Ima turned and shook Katja's hand off of her shoulder. She tried to walk away, but Katja grabbed her shirt and flung her around so that Ima was facing her. "I am telling you something, Ima, and you'd better listen to me. Your life is at stake. I can't save you unless you let me help you."

Ima shrugged.

"Ima!" Katja yelled, but Ima just stared at her blindly. Finally, Katja released her grip, and Ima went into her room and slammed the door behind her.

Katja could not tell the women in her organization about her daughter. She was ashamed. If the other women knew the shameful things that Ima was doing, there would be no way back for Ima. She would become the center of malicious gossip. Ima would never have decent friends again, and her chances of marrying a nice boy would diminish completely.

Katja didn't want to burden her mother any further. Zofia had enough trouble fighting to stay healthy and didn't need to discuss upsetting things. When Katja was with Zofia, she tried to make light of Ima's situation. The radiation treatments had been hard enough on Zofia. She was still having difficulty eating, and even now, sometimes Katja could hear Zofia in the bathroom vomiting.

The thought of losing her mother terrified Katja. Most of the day, she prayed silently for her daughter, her mother, and even John. John was the only person to whom she could open her ravaged heart. She told him everything, and he listened. His calm helped her to quiet her trembling insides. There was not much advice John could give her, but just having someone she could trust, someone who would not use the knowledge of Ima's descent into Hell against her, was enough.

One Sunday afternoon, Katja and John stayed much longer than usual at the park. It was an afternoon when the sun kissed the thick grass and the leaves on the trees. The sky was a pale silver blue with clouds that looked like swirls of cotton candy. Katja was in better spirits than usual as she told John how much better her mother was doing. But she said Ima was a volcano that could erupt at any time. John just nodded. There was nothing to be said. They sat quietly for a moment. Then John told Katja about his work. John was winning the case, and his firm was pleased with him.

"I suppose I've proven myself worthy. They gave me a raise," John said.

"That's wonderful. You must be ecstatic."

"Yes. It's nice to be appreciated, but there is a price to pay. They want me to come back to England. I won't be here much longer," he said with a sad smile.

She nodded. Katja had forgotten that the time would come when John would have to return home. She felt a cloud of sadness, and her heart felt empty. It was a feeling of loss she had not ever even considered. The time she'd had with John filled a void inside her. "How soon will you be leaving?"

"I'm not sure, but less than a month."

"Oh," Katja nodded and swallowed hard.

He leaned forward and kissed her. She smelled his cologne. It had been long since she had been this close to a man.

"I've come to care a lot for you, Katja."

"I care for you, too, John."

"I guess what I am trying to say is that I think I could be falling in love with you," he said.

She cleared her throat.

"Would you consider moving to England?"

"I don't know. I mean, my organization, my mother, and my daughter are here. I don't think I could do that, John."

"Are your feelings for me strong enough that you think it might be a good idea for me to apply for work here in Israel?"

"You mean you want to stay? Permanently?"

"Yes, if you want me to."

She did. She wanted him to stay. "Yes, I do want you to stay. I would miss you terribly if you left."

"Then I will see what I can do to change jobs."

CHAPTER EIGHT

John began to apply for work at Israeli law firms. As he expected, it was not easy. But he was used to rejection. He'd been fighting his entire life and would not stop now. One afternoon, he had several job interviews lined up and asked Katja to meet him at a café in the city instead of at the park. That way, he would be able to see her for a half hour between meetings with potential employers. She agreed. Then she realized that this was the first time they'd ever actually been out together.

Katja arrived first. He was late. She assumed that John's interview had taken longer than expected. So, she ordered a glass of white wine and waited. A woman, who was a less active member of her organization, was seated at a table a few feet away. She was sitting with another female friend whom Katja didn't recognize. As soon as she saw Katja, she got up and came over to say hello.

"Katja, how are you?"

"I'm fine. Doing great." Katja's voice uncontrollably went up a few octaves. She forced a smile. Damn, what was this woman's name?

"How's your mother?"

"She's all right. She's been sick, but she's doing better."

"I'm so sorry to hear that."

"Thank you, but she's doing better." Katja wished that this woman without a name would leave.

"And Ima? How is she? Sari says she hasn't seen her at school. Has she been ill?"

Katja had hired a private tutor for Ima. But most of the time, Ima did not allow the tutor into her room. Katja knew Ima was not attending school, but what could she tell this woman? What could she say? *Please, go away. Go back to your table with your friend and stop asking many questions.*

"No," Katja coughed. "No, she's not ill. She's been taking classes abroad," Katja lied. If someone saw Ima on the street, her deception would be exposed. Dear Lord, Katja wished this woman would leave her in peace.

"Really? That's so exciting. You mean she's doing some kind of high school exchange program?"

"Yes, something like that."

Katja saw John walk in, and she was relieved. The hostess directed him to where she was waiting. Now that John had arrived, perhaps this questioning woman would be on her way.

"Hi, Katja," John said, with a big smile on his strong, handsome face.

The woman looked at Katja, shocked and stunned. For a moment, Katja didn't understand. It had been a long time since she and John had been meeting, and during that time, Katja had stopped seeing the difference in their skin color. From the look on the woman's face, she was reminded.

"Oh, your friend is here." The woman without a name's voice cracked. "I'll let you two enjoy lunch," she said. Then she walked back to the table and whispered something to her friend. Her friend's face contorted, and she whispered something back. They shook their heads but moved closer together, whispering and bonding as they discussed what they were sure would become the latest scandal. Katja could see that they were gossiping about her.

John sat down, but it was hard not to notice everyone in the restaurant staring at them. Even the waitress, although she tried to hide her distaste, seemed uncomfortable.

"Can I take your order?"

"I think we'll need a minute," John said.

Katja was trying not to look around at the faces of the other patrons. She could feel the heaviness of their stares. They were judging her, scrutinizing her. John studied Katja as she opened the menu. If she met John's gaze, she knew he would see how affected she was by the humiliating gawking.

The waitress returned, and they ordered. Then, neither of them spoke. Katja glanced up at John and saw the pain in his face. She knew that he could read what she was thinking and what she was feeling.

John cleared his throat. "I guess we make quite a pair. These folks have probably never seen a white woman with a black man before."

"I don't know what I was thinking when we decided to meet here. I don't know why, but I wasn't expecting such a reaction from all these strangers."

"They don't know any better. All they know is what they've been taught, and they've been taught that races or religions are not supposed to mix. They think that people are different and should stay with their own."

"John, I stopped seeing your color months ago. I know this sounds crazy, but I forgot how prejudiced people can be. And the worst part is that most of them are Jews. They should know about prejudice. For God's sake, they've endured enough of it to know."

"What they think isn't important to me. How do you feel about it, Kat? That's what really matters. What these people think is their problem. How do you feel? That's what you have to ask yourself."

The food arrived, but Katja's appetite was gone. She moved the salad around on her plate and noticed that everyone who came into the restaurant looked at her and John. The people walking by on the sidewalk turned to look. It was impossible to ignore their disapproval.

"How did the interview go?" she asked.

"I think it went well. But I'm not so sure that you want me to move to Israel. Are you still sure you want to pursue this? You and me, I mean."

"I know what you mean," Katja said. She felt a tear slip down her cheek. She'd spent her entire life trying to fit in, trying to win the approval of everyone she knew. Now, she was doing something that was clearly forbidden. A relationship with a black man would certainly draw attention to her.

What was she thinking when she told John she wanted him to move to Israel? Did she somehow believe that people would accept them as a couple, or was she stupidly blinded by her emotions? "I need time to think, John. I can't say how I feel right now because I don't know. I guess I was naïve. I never thought about how we would be treated. I only thought about how happy you make me and how you fill my life with friendship and caring."

"And I will continue to fill your life with beautiful things if you let me."

"I have to go, John. I have to think."

"Please, Kat, don't let people who don't know or care about either of us ruin this chance we have for happiness. Don't do it. I'm begging you."

A tear splashed from Katja's eye onto the white tablecloth, and then it expanded just enough to leave a small pear-shaped mark. Katja stood up. "I'm sorry, John. I have to go," she said again, and then she left.

He sat at the table, alone, with his full plate in front of him. John could not eat, but he also could not leave. His body was frozen with grief. He had been foolish to allow himself to believe that he would be blessed with happiness from being with a white woman as a man and wife. He, of all people, should have known that the world would come between them.

CHAPTER NINE

THE FOLLOWING DAY, a dark, gray sky poured torrents of rain over Tel Aviv. Rains like these were not common events in Israel. The sheets of water came down in angles, and the sun refused to make an appearance at all.

Ima had not come home the previous night. The lengths of her absences were growing. Because of this, it was hard to say when she might return, if at all. Katja had tried locking Ima in her room, but she climbed out the window. Katja had even gone so far as to hire a man to come and nail Ima's window shut, but it did nothing.

Ima waited until Katja and Zofia were asleep, and then she left by the front door. The only option Katja could think of to save her daughter was institutionalizing her, but Zofia was terrified.

"Once you put her in a crazy house, she will carry that stigma for the rest of her life. People will treat her differently. She'll have trouble getting jobs, getting married, everything. Don't do it, Katja. We have to work this out on our own," Zofia said.

Katja reluctantly agreed. Every day that went by, Ima was in danger. Ima had no regard for her life. It seemed to Katja that her daughter was on a suicidal path, and no one could stop her. "I have to do something, Mother. She isn't going to make it if I don't. She's taking drugs, and God only knows where she gets all the money in her room. If she sleeps with men for money, she could run into a dangerous one, and anything could happen. I don't know when the last time was that she went to school."

"Yes, all that is true, and the tutor isn't working. Ima won't even study with her," Zofia said. "I am at a loss here."

"I'm going to try another therapist. That's all I can do. But all I know, Mama, is that I have to do something. I can't just sit back and let her destroy herself. Just look at her. She's so skinny she looks like a scarecrow, with all that black makeup all over her eyes and her hair chopped off. Oh, mama, our Ima is in trouble."

"I know, I know," Zofia said.

Katja hated to burden her mother. Zofia's skin was almost as gray as the sky outside. She was also scarecrow-thin, and Katja knew how hard it was for her to keep food or water down.

Katja wished that she could talk to John. He was a warm blanket for her in this cold and terrible world. And yet, she was afraid, afraid of what people would say if she were to join her life with the life of a man of color.

Yesterday, she'd felt the heavy hand of bigotry and judgment weigh upon her neck, bending her head and mind down to its will. She'd walked out on him, leaving him alone in a restaurant to face the angry stares. She could call him, but there was nothing to say. She didn't have the courage it would take to weather the hatred of an interracial marriage. And now John was gone. Katja felt alone and empty as she got up to make a pot of tea and tried to entice her mother to have some breakfast.

She had never told Zofia about John. In fact, until yesterday, nobody had known about the friendship that Katja and John shared. It was easier that way, but not realistic. They couldn't spend the rest of their lives meeting in a park if they were to go forward with their relationship. The alternative was too hard to face.

"Mama, have some warm pita?"

Zofia nodded her head. "A quarter of a piece. That's enough."

"I bought some lovely dried fruit. Will you have a little?"

"No, not today. It has a funny aftertaste to me," Zofia said.

Katja felt the familiar pang of fear shoot through her again. Any day, she could lose her mother. At any hour, she could lose her daughter. Nothing felt safe, and nothing felt secure—nothing but John, and now she would have to get over him. Katja knew herself and was too weak to bear the shame, stares, and humiliation. She had been so careful to avoid anyone finding out about her secret, horrific bloodline. And she hid all of it because she had wanted so much to be accepted. So how could she possibly bring such negative attention to herself now?

She couldn't. She would rather endure the pain of loss than face the criticism, and right now, she despised herself for her weakness.

CHAPTER TEN

A YEAR LATER, Ima walked out into traffic and was hit by a car. It was fortunate that the automobile was moving slowly. Ima was not seriously hurt, but Katja was terribly shaken by the incident.

It was hard to determine if Ima was attempting suicide, if she was out of her mind on drugs, or if the whole thing was an accident. The staff at the hospital drew Ima's blood. It determined that Ima had not recently ingested any illegal substances. Still, she did have traces in her blood of having taken drugs in the previous days.

Katja stood at Ima's bedside and broke down into tears. There was nothing she could do for her daughter, nothing at all. The sweet child whom she and Mendel had adored was disintegrating before her eyes, and all she could do was weep. Ima turned away from her mother. She would not look at Katja, and this broke Katja's heart even more.

"What can I do for you, Ima? How can I help you?" Katja begged through heart-wrenching tears, but Ima would not answer.

Katja decided that she had no choice. If she wanted to save her daughter's life, she must sign Ima into a mental ward before things escalated to the point of no return. Zofia finally agreed.

Zofia's cancer was in remission, and she was feeling stronger.

She wanted to finish her memoirs quickly but could not focus on anything but Ima.

After the accident, the hospital kept Ima overnight to ensure she did not have a concussion. When Katja arrived the following day, she decided that she must tell Ima what she planned to do.

"How do you feel?"

"I'm okay," Ima said, her voice small. The childlike tone reminded Katja of Ima as a toddler, and she almost began to weep again.

"Ima, your grandmother and I are very worried about you."

"I'm fine. There's nothing to worry about."

"Ima, you're not fine. You're nowhere near fine," Katja said, her voice cracking. "I love you. Bubbie loves you, too. We want to help you."

"I said, don't worry about me. I'm fine."

Katja took a deep breath. "We're going to put you in a hospital. A hospital for people who have problems. It's a place where you'll be safe. A place where you can get some help."

"No, I don't want to go to a hospital. How dare you try to put me in a nuthouse? I'm not going."

"You are, if I say you are. You're still a seventeen-year-old child, and you'll do as I say." Katja's face was beet red.

"I won't stay. I'll run away."

"Ima! Listen to me."

"Please, Mommy, please don't lock me up. Please, I promise I'll do better. I'll stop taking drugs. I'll stop doing bad things. I'll go and talk to the therapist like you wanted me to. Please, Mommy, please give me another chance."

Katja felt her throat close. She knew she should go ahead with her plan, but she couldn't bear to think of Ima locked up in a room, maybe in a straitjacket.

"You promise me, Ima? You promise to try, to really try?"

"Yes, I promise, Mama. I do, I promise."

CHAPTER ELEVEN

At first, Ima seemed to be serious about changing. She was trying to act the part, getting home at reasonable hours, attending sessions with her tutor, seeing a therapist regularly, and dressing less provocatively. Zofia saw through Ima and prayed she was wrong, but she was a pretty good judge of character. She felt it was only a matter of time, and over the next year, Ima's troubles only increased.

If it had not been for the IDF, Ima might not have made it into adulthood alive. However, at eighteen, like all other Israelis, Ima was drafted. Katja was worried about how Ima might fare in the IDF, but Zofia was relieved.

"This is what she needs," Zofia said. "You'll see."

"I hope you're right, Mama."

The IDF was Ima's worst nightmare. She fought against the constant demands and restrictions, but the Israeli army was stronger. They saw a troubled girl but were unwilling to give up on her. They'd dealt with this sort of thing before. So, the IDF sent her to a special unit where she received tough but effective training.

CHAPTER TWELVE

Katja had not received any correspondence from Ima since she had left for the army. Every week, Katja sent letter after letter, but Ima never answered. Katja even wrote to her squadron leader just to see if Ima was all right. She received a brief and to-the-point answer that Ima was doing fine.

All communication was cut off. Katja felt as if she might go mad with worry.

Then, the most remarkable thing happened. Ima would be finished serving her term with the IDF in six months when Katja received a letter from her. Katja knew Ima's handwriting, so she immediately knew who the letter was from. She tore the envelope open. Her hands trembled, but seeing her baby's handwriting brought hope to her heart. Then she plopped down in the chair as she read the following words in amazement:

Dear Mom and Bubbie,

I just signed up for a second term in the IDF. The army has been a great experience for me. I met someone. He is the love of my life. His name is Ido, and I know you will both love him. This is going to sound a little strange, but we got married in a civil ceremony. Believe me, I know it was the right thing to do. I've messed up a lot of things in my life, but this isn't one of them. Ido has helped me to realize how much I've hurt both of you over the years, and I am really sorry. I hope you can forgive me.

Ido and I are coming to see both of you next week. We will only have a week to spend with you because although we have a longer leave, we've signed up for an extra assignment. The assignment pays well, and we could use the extra money since we want to buy a small house. The assignment seems like fun, actually. We are going to be escorting a group of American teenagers from a synagogue in the U.S. all around Israel. This should be interesting! Anyway, Ido and I look forward to seeing you both. By the way, my new name is Ima Hadar! Can you believe it?

Love to you both,

Ima

Katja drew a deep breath. Was this for the better? It was hard to say. Ima had always been so unstable, and to Katja, this letter seemed that Ima was still unstable. She read it to Zofia.

"Well, I am not sure what to say. We will know more once we meet the boy and see them together."

"She sounds like she's still crazy but in a different way," Katja said.

"Maybe so, but then again, maybe not. All we can do is pray," Zofia said.

When Ima and Ido arrived, Zofia instantly saw the change in Ima. She'd gone from being a troubled girl into a confident young woman. Katja saw the changes, too. She was dressed conservatively, and her hair was cut and groomed. This was not the same Ima.

Ido treated Ima like a treasure, but Katja saw too many similarities between Ido and her ex-fiancé, Elan. This bothered Katja a little. Katja had suffered a terribly broken heart over Elan and was afraid for Ima.

She talked to Zofia, and they decided that Ido must never learn the truth about Katja's birth parents. He must never know that Ima's grandparents were Germans and her grandfather was an SS officer. That had destroyed the relationship between Katja and Elan. Katja and Zofia knew Ima was not strong enough to endure a breakup between herself and Ido. It would destroy her. Katja and Zofia knew they must keep the secret from Ido, no matter the cost.

The week that Ima and Ido stayed with Ima's mother and grandmother was the most joyous time Zofia could remember spending with Ima since she was a baby. Ima was happy. In fact, she seemed to be like the old Ima, the Ima before the incident. She was helpful, considerate, and caring. Who was this girl?

This girl no longer chopped her hair or wore thick black eye makeup. Ima was beautiful, her blond hair long and flowing in loose curls. She'd put on just enough weight for a slim but healthy figure. It made Zofia smile, and secretly, when she was alone at night, she would speak quietly to Isaac, who she felt was always with her.

"It looks like Ima is going to be all right, Isaac. Now, if only my Katja were not so all alone. I worry. When the time comes for me to leave the earth and finally come home to you, who will be here for my Katja?"

CHAPTER THIRTEEN

Two DAYS after Ima and Ido left, Katja was feeling lonely. Zofia was with her, but when Ima and Ido were visiting the house, it seemed to come alive. They were young and filled the usually quiet house with life and exuberance.

Although Katja had filled the house with food before they arrived, the refrigerator was now empty. She opened the door and looked inside, then smiled to herself. When she and Zofia were alone, most of the food they bought went to waste. Neither of them ate much anymore.

Oh well, she would get dressed and go to the market early before she went into her office. Katja slipped on her jeans and a silky white blouse with thick shoulder pads. Because she was slender with very small shoulders, the new style looked good on her. Most of her friends who wore the shoulder pads looked like football players. She wore a pair of black pumps with a kitten heel, but instead of fluffing her hair up to look full and teased like she usually did, she put it into a French braid and wore her gold hoop earrings.

It was early, so the food market was not as busy as usual. However, several women were talking and complaining about rising food costs. She was glad that she didn't know any of them. She would have had to stay polite and listen if she knew one of them.

Katja was walking down one of the aisles, looking for the olive oil she bought. She was quite particular about her choice. It had to be extra virgin, dark green, and good quality. The brand she used was sold out, so she scrutinized the others, trying to decide which would suffice when she looked up and saw John.

It had been a long time since that day she'd left him in the café. A shiver went down her spine. He was pushing a steel grocery cart and walking toward her. She felt such a mixture of emotions that she could not even determine what she was feeling.

She wanted to rush into his arms at the sight of his large, comfortable frame and wide smile. But then, she was reminded of why they'd separated in the first place, and her heart fell. Was he married? The thought of him being married to someone else cut her deeply. But of course, why wouldn't he have married? She'd left him. What did she expect?

The women had somehow come around the corner, and now they were standing like a group of nosey hens and watching her. Their judgmental looks reminded her that she and John were of different races. But even so, here he was. John, her friend. John, the man who loved her without question, regardless of who she was or where she came from. God, how she'd missed him.

"How have you been, Katja?" His voice brought back so many memories. It was gentle, kind, understanding.

"Fine…" she stammered.

"I've missed you."

She cleared her throat. "I thought you were going back to England."

"Yes, I did go back. Then, I got an offer from one of the firms I had applied to when I was here, and it was a great offer. So, I'm living here in Israel now." He smiled at her, but she could see the pain in his eyes—pain she'd caused. "Are you still living in the same place?" he asked.

"Yes. I'm still living in the same place. I'm still volunteering with The Wives of Fallen Soldiers."

She quickly glanced at the selections in his cart. It was hard to determine if he was shopping for one or more.

He nodded. The conversation was awkward, but he didn't want to say goodbye.

"I read in the local paper that The Wives of Fallen Soldiers is doing a benefit this week to raise money for the organization?"

"Yes, we are. In fact, we're featuring performances by the kids from the local school. We've done this before. The parents come and buy tickets. They enjoy seeing their kids on stage. It guarantees us at least some audience. I think it's going to be a lot of fun.

"We have a troupe of fourth-grade girls who are members of a ballet troupe who will be doing a performance from *Romeo and Juliet*." After she'd said that, she felt her face flush. How clumsy —*Romeo and Juliet*. She wondered if he'd caught the connection. Again, Katja cleared her throat. "And we'll have a band from a local high school doing a few numbers. There'll be nobody famous, but a few of the local restaurants are donating food."

"It sounds like you've put together a nice fundraiser."

"I hope so. There will be a few other performers, too. All of them are local kids. We even have a rock and roll band made up of kids from the high school. It looks like they have a lot of fans because tickets are almost sold out. Anyway, the money goes to a good cause." She felt like she was rambling but didn't want to say goodbye.

"Katja," he said.

She heard the hesitation in his voice, and she wanted to run. She was terrified of what he might say but wanted to stay, too.

"Katja," he repeated. "Can I call you sometime?"

God, how she wanted to say yes. In fact, she wanted to leave her cart in the aisle and go with him right now. Run away with him to some secluded island where nobody could stand in judgment of them. But she said, "I don't know, John. I don't think so. It's not a good idea."

He nodded. She felt her heart sink as she looked into his eyes.

"I understand," he said, looking down. Then he met her gaze again. "Listen, you probably will never use this card, but if you ever need anything, anything at all, here is my number. Just call me. I'll always be there for you, Kat."

His hands trembled as he took a business card from his worn, brown-leather wallet and handed it to her.

"It was good to see you, John," she said, slipping the card into her purse and trying to hide the tears that were stinging the corners of her eyes.

He watched her walk away. Then he left his shopping cart where it was. The hell with the food. He'd get takeout again this week. John had to get out of there quickly. He didn't want anyone to see the pain in his face.

CHAPTER FOURTEEN

ELAN FELT a smile wash over his face as he watched Noa practicing for her ballet recital. This had to be at least the one-hundredth time she'd gone over her dance in the last two days. Even though the constant repetitive music on the tape player drove him nuts, he was proud of her.

She looked so much like her mother, but Elan had to admit she danced like her father. Elan had always been a good dancer, but ballet wasn't for him. Elan Amsel had fallen head-first in love with rock and roll from the first time he'd heard it. He still loved it, and even though he was over fifty, he could still out-jitterbug most people half his age.

Unfortunately, no one danced the jitterbug in any of the night-clubs anymore. But at home, Elan would turn on the radio and dance with his daughter. He'd taught her how to swing, spin, and follow his lead as he lifted her high into the air. She could move in his arms effortlessly. It was easy for Noa to master any dance, from Latin to waltz, but she longed to be a prima ballerina.

It was her dream, and she wanted it more than anything in the world. That was why she was so excited when she was selected to dance the part of Juliet. Noa Amsel had won the female lead in the fourth-grade performance. And now The Wives of Fallen Soldiers was doing a benefit featuring the ballet at the local community center. It was important to Noa, and she was determined to be perfect. It was the first time she'd ever danced in front of a big crowd, and she was a nervous wreck.

Gloria Finkelstein was still working for the Amsels, although now she was more like a grandmother than an employee. Elan still felt he needed to keep her on because sometimes his job took him away overnight. Although he knew he could always leave Noa with his brother- and sister-in-law, he preferred Mrs. Finkelstein. He liked the confidence of knowing that Noa was at home in bed, especially when she had to go to school in the morning.

It was two more days until the performance. Elan could see that as the time to perform got closer, Noa became more on edge. He would be glad when it was over and things at home could return to normal.

The dancers were to have a rehearsal at the auditorium the night before the performance to help them become familiar with the stage where they would be dancing. Elan promised Noa he would be home from work on time to accompany her to the rehearsal. The dancers were scheduled to be at the venue at five o'clock. He had to leave an hour early to make it on time, but for Noa, he would do anything.

Noa was ready and anxious to go when Elan got home. She had her little pink bag with her costume and ballet slippers packed. Her hair was neatly pulled into a tight bun on the top of her head.

"Just give me ten minutes to shower and change, and we can be on our way," Elan said, kissing Noa's head.

"Hurry, Daddy, I don't want to be late."

"I know you don't, and I promise we will be on time." He smiled at her and patted her cheek.

Noa's ballet instructor was waiting at the community center to greet them when Elan and Noa arrived. She introduced herself to Elan, showed Noa how to get to the dressing room, and escorted Elan to the audience seats.

"The rehearsal should start in about a half hour. Just make yourself comfortable. There is coffee and cake in the lobby."

"Thank you," Elan said. He could use a cup of strong coffee.

The parents of the students who were performing had gathered in the lobby. They were nibbling on individual cakes and sipping coffee. Elan poured a cup of black, steaming-hot coffee. As he turned around to join the other parents, he saw that golden blond halo of curls that he knew could belong to only one person: his old love, Katja.

He stood dumbfounded—it was her.

His eyes were glued to her as he spilled the scalding coffee on his thumb. A shot of pain shook him out of his dream state. He wanted to speak to her but wasn't sure what to say. What could he possibly say? So much had happened. Perhaps it was best to go back into the auditorium and hide in the dark, in the back row, until he could figure out what he wanted to do. But in an instant, it was too late. Their eyes met, and she saw him.

"Elan?" Katja asked, her head cocking to one side and her mouth gaping open.

Could she still be so pretty? How could she still look the same as she did twenty years ago? He was suddenly aware of how much he'd aged.

"Katja…" He tried to sound casual and tried to muster a smile.

"What are you doing here?" she asked.

"My daughter is in the school ballet." He looked into those azure eyes, and he remembered everything. The first time they made love, the night he proposed, the breakup, the shiva for Mendel…

"Oh, how nice? Who is your daughter?" Katja said, unsure of what else to say. Elan had a child, a girl. Did he have more children? She was surprised, stunned. *Of course,* she thought, *why wouldn't he have gotten married and had children?* It was just so hard to believe. To her, he was still Elan, young Elan, the Elan she'd once been engaged to marry. But of course, he wasn't. Too many years had passed. Even so, there was no doubt Elan was still handsome, strong, and sexy. The same on the outside, anyway.

"Noa Amsel. She's playing Juliet."

"Oh, you must be so proud!" Katja said, forcing an uncomfortable smile to hide her awkwardness. "I'll have to keep an eye on her performance." Katja coughed a little. "So, is your wife here?"

"No." Elan looked away. "My wife passed away."

"I'm sorry." Katja wanted to know how, why, and who she was. Who was the woman who had been good enough for Elan when she had not been? She longed to ask, but how could she pry? The poor woman was dead. And besides, she wasn't even sure why she wanted to know in the first place.

"It was a long time ago, nine years. She died in childbirth."

"Oh…" Katja felt her throat close. That was horrible, a young woman dying in childbirth. She thought about Ima. Someday soon, Ima might become pregnant. God forbid anything like that should happen to Ima. Katja was quickly repentant for the terrible thoughts she'd been having about Elan's wife. *I'm sorry*, she whispered in her head. *God forgive me.*

"Oh, Elan, I really am so sorry…"

He nodded and shrugged his shoulders. What was there to say? He'd lost his wife, his best friend, and now the first woman he'd ever loved was gazing at him with pity in her eyes. Elan Amsel hated to be pitied. It made him feel weak. There was nothing worse to him than to look weak in the eyes of others, especially women and, even more devastating, the woman he had once loved.

The lights in the small auditorium began to flicker. A woman's voice came over the loudspeaker.

"Ladies and gentlemen, please take your seats. The dress rehearsal is about to start!"

All the parents began saying their goodbyes and shuffling into the auditorium.

"I guess I'd better go," Elan said.

"Yes. The show will start in just a few minutes."

"Good to see you, Kat."

"Yes, good to see you too, Elan.

During the show, Elan was distracted by memories. Noa would glance out into the audience to catch her father's eye. Elan would smile back at her with encouragement, but he could not overcome the emptiness deep within his belly. What was it about Katja?

Perhaps it was best to go back into the auditorium and hide in the dark, in the back row, until he could figure out what he wanted to do. But then, when he saw her again, all the feelings he'd once had returned as if they'd never left him.

Noa was ranting with excitement, telling Mrs. Finkelstein all about her show. Elan was doing his best to appear involved, but his heart and mind were elsewhere.

It was a relief when Noa finally went to bed, and Elan didn't have to hide his distress. He took a hot shower, hoping it would relax him enough to fall asleep. Finally, he lay down and stared at the ceiling.

A glimmer of light from the silver moon filtered in through the window. His mind was on overdrive, and he couldn't slow it down. He remembered Nina's soft, flowing hair, the way she would shake her head and laugh at him. She was the most like him of any woman he'd ever known. Without question, he'd loved her. But Nina was gone, and nothing he could do would change that.

Elan was terribly lonely. His memories of Katja reminded him of just how alone he was. She might be the only woman on earth who could still make him believe that loving was worth the pain of losing a loved one. Lying in bed only made him feel clammy and restless. It was better to get up and sit in the living room.

Staring out the window at the shadows the bushes and palm trees cast upon the ground, Elan managed to drink enough bourbon to fall asleep in the chair.

Then, as he slept, Nina came to him in a dream. It was not unusual for him to have dreams about Nina that were so real that when he awoke, he would have tears in his eyes, wishing he could sleep forever. In his dreams, he could feel her hand on his face, her soft voice in his ear, and his longing to be with her would overwhelm him.

But tonight, when Nina came in his sleep, Elan told her about seeing Katja. She said she understood his feelings and told him she knew he needed someone. Nina said that it hurt her to see him so alone. "You should be with someone, Elan…it would be good for you. You may not realize it, but it would be good for Noa, too. Think about it.

"She needs a female role model, not just Mrs. Finkelstein, but a younger woman who will more easily understand what it is like to be a young girl growing up. After all, as you know, the years pass quickly. Before you know it, Noa will be a teenager. If you want my opinion, I think you should ask Katja to have dinner with you. Maybe there is something left of what you once had together to salvage."

"Nina, you know that you have my heart. But you're right. Katja still has a piece of my heart, too. I think that once you love someone, a part of you will always love them. Not that she could ever take your place. Nobody could ever take your place."

"Yes, Elan, it's true. Once you love someone, there is always something that you will share with them, but you've been mourning me for too long. It's time…"

"Nina, Nina…" he said.

"It's time, Elan. It's time for you, and it's time for Noa…"

So, the following day, when Noa went backstage to prepare for her performance, Elan asked the woman at the ticket counter if she knew where Katja was.

"Yes, she's probably in the back, helping the students get ready. Do you need to see her?"

"I do. Can you ask her to come out, please? I will only need a moment of her time."

"All right. Wait here."

Katja came out from the back of the stage. Her lovely cream-colored skin was flushed to a soft, blush-pink, and her eyes were bright with the excitement that was so contagious from all the performing students.

"Katja," Elan said, smiling. His palms were sweating. She might reject him.

"It's you? Mara said someone wanted to talk to me," Katja said, smiling. "What can I do for you, Elan?"

"Yes, I just wanted to talk to you for a minute." He suddenly felt foolish. "But I was not thinking. I can see that you're busy. This is probably a bad time."

"No, it's fine. What is it, Elan?"

"I feel so strange asking you this, Kat, but will you have dinner with me?"

The papers she was holding in her hand dropped to the floor. She bent to pick them up. Elan could see that her hands were trembling. He bent to help her. "I can't tonight. There will be so much to do after the show is over," she said. Katja wasn't sure what she felt or what she wanted. What to do. Buy time, buy time to think. She wanted to ask him a million questions, but she said nothing.

"Tomorrow, then?" He cleared his throat and bit his lower lip. "Please? Tomorrow night?"

"Okay, yes, okay. Tomorrow."

CHAPTER FIFTEEN

THE FOLLOWING DAY, Elan couldn't eat anything at all. He went to work, but his mind was miles away, continuously going over the possible conversations that might take place tonight. Tonight, at dinner, he would tell Katja everything he felt and all of his regrets.

It would not be easy to admit to being wrong. He had never been good at acknowledging his imperfections. But life had certainly proven to him that he wasn't as invincible as he'd thought he was when he was young. Over the years, Elan had made many terrible mistakes: he'd hurt so many people. He'd been selfish, stubborn, and self-righteous. He'd never believed that he needed anyone but himself.

But he thought God must have been laughing because God intervened and sent Nina into his life. That was when he truly learned what it meant to love. That love made him tender and vulnerable, and the pain of losing Nina had brought him to his knees. It hurt more than anything he'd ever felt. Even so, he would not trade a single moment of the time he'd spent with Nina. All the pain was worth the incredible joy.

Yes, Elan Amsel was a much different man than the arrogant boy who'd turned his back on Katja right before their wedding because she wasn't born of Jewish blood. Life had kicked him in the stomach, and he'd learned just how defenseless he really was against the will of God.

Perhaps he and Katja still had a chance at a future together, Elan thought. When Nina died, he'd lost all sexual desire until he saw Katja again. Amazingly, even after all the years that had passed, Kat was still so beautiful. Even though he'd left her, she'd always kept a special place in his heart. Could it be possible? Could Elan have another chance at happiness?

Katja had always been so forgiving, so easygoing, and a good and kind person. She would be a good wife and a wonderful mother to Noa. When he thought of Katja, he couldn't help but remember how she was always willing to give of herself. He wasn't surprised that she was at the forefront of developing the charitable organization. It would be like her to extend a hand to help others who suffered in the same way that she did when she lost Mendel.

He planned to pick Katja up at eight that night. Hoping to rekindle tender feelings from the past, Elan made a reservation at the restaurant where they went to dinner for the first time. They went out together back in the nineteen-sixties. It was surprising that the place was still open. When he called to make the reservation, he requested the same table that they'd shared so many years ago.

On his way home from work that night, Elan picked up a dozen roses for Katja. He'd given her roses when they first met but couldn't remember the color. The florist had a choice of pink or yellow. He decided on pink. Then he went home and got ready. He informed Mrs. Finkelstein that he would not be home until late.

As always, she assured him that she would take care of everything. Noa would have a healthy dinner, do her homework, and go to bed at a reasonable hour. Before Elan left the house, he looked in the mirror. *Not bad for a man of fifty-three*, he thought. His body was still in good shape, even if his hair was almost all gray. At least it hadn't thinned. Elan's face was still handsome, his jaw still strong, and his ebony eyes still piercing. Satisfied with his appearance, Elan took the bouquet off the counter and left to pick up Katja.

CHAPTER SIXTEEN

KATJA TOLD Zofia that she was having dinner with Elan. Zofia didn't say a word. She just cocked her head and looked at her daughter with that knowing look that only a mother who knew her child very well could deliver. That look made Katja think twice about what she was doing. Then Zofia, without saying a word, went into her bedroom. Katja knew that her mother was tired and would probably take a nap.

Flinging the white French doors of her closet open wide, Katja studied her clothing choices for the night. She didn't want Elan to think that she'd made a great effort to see him. She wanted to appear casual. But still, she wanted to look her best. So, what should she wear? A dress, even a sundress, was too much. She would wear black jeans with a blue cotton sweater that matched her eyes.

Earlier that day, Katja had made an emergency appointment with her hairdresser, where her hair was blown out and then curled at the ends. It looked perfect. She carefully applied light, natural-looking makeup and slipped into her pumps with the small heels. High heels would have looked like she'd tried too hard.

The full-length mirror on the back of the door to Katja's bedroom confirmed that she looked good. She bit her lower lip.

Elan Amsel—he'd haunted her for her entire life. She had never stopped loving him. Not even through the years of her marriage to Mendel, not ever. What was it about him? His crazy good looks? His passion? His arrogance? Damn him.

The doorbell rang. No matter where he went, Elan was always on time. Katja remembered that from long ago when they were a couple.

Before she could face him, Katja took a deep breath. Then she picked up her purse and put her small cosmetic bag inside. When she did, she noticed John's card. It was in the center pocket where she always kept her cosmetic bag. A strange feeling she could not explain or understand came over her. John? It would be good to talk to John about all of this. What was she feeling? But right now, there was no time to assess her emotions. Elan knocked again. He was at the door.

With a trembling hand, Katja turned the knob and opened the door.

Elan stood there, smiling. His dark eyes twinkled, and his perfect white teeth sparkled. Damn him. Elan Amsel. Arrogant, Elan Amsel. He knew he was handsome. There was no doubt about that.

When Elan handed the bouquet of pink roses to Katja, the gesture touched her deeply. It brought back memories, so many memories, both good and bad.

"Oh, Elan, thank you." She turned and took a vase off the shelf, then filled it with water and put the flowers in the vase.

He smiled, and his eyes roamed her body from the top of her head to her feet. She saw the admiration in his face. "You look beautiful."

She turned away; she knew her cheeks were flushed.

"Come," he said, taking her arm. "Let's go and have dinner."

———

Katja had not been to the restaurant where Elan had taken her for over twenty years. The last time she was here was a night when she and Elan were a couple, and they were dining here together. In fact, she could remember clearly that it was only a week before that terrible day when Manfred Blau was arrested after he escaped from prison in Germany and brought back to Israel for trial. It was the day that Katja's life had changed forever.

Katja and Elan were expecting company for dinner. She'd been in the kitchen preparing food while Elan was still at work. The television in the living room had been on. She'd been half-listening to the news of Manfred Blau, the SS officer's trial. Blau, who was being interviewed on TV, mentioned his betrayal by Zofia at the Nuremberg trials and about his wife's death shortly after the trial due to cancer. He told how he and his wife adopted a Lebensborn child, and they named her Katja, but he didn't know what had become of her after his trial.

Katja heard his words and ran into the living room to turn the volume up to be sure she'd not been mistaken. She had not. From that moment on, Katja's life had never been the same. Katja was not the daughter of Zofia and Isaac Zuckerman. She was the child of Nazis.

Zofia confirmed it was true and showed her the Lebensborn papers Blau's wife Christa had given her when she bade her to take her away. Katja knew she had to tell Elan. Though it had been on television, it was unlikely anyone would make the connection. But they might, and she had to come clean with Elan, or she would live with that specter over her head forever.

When Elan learned the truth about Katja, he'd walked away from her as if their love had never existed, leaving her a broken woman.

Now, she sat across from the man who remained fused into the cracks he'd made in her heart so long ago. How could he still be so good-looking at his age, confident, so damned sexy? He was still Elan. Why had she agreed to have dinner with him? The memories were attacking her mind like swords.

The waitress strolled over to the table, trying not to look overeager to take their order. Although she held the menu open in front of her, Katja had not read a word.

"Can I take your order?" the young girl asked as she held a pencil and pad.

"I'm sorry, I'm not ready. Can I have another minute? Please."

"Of course. I'll be back."

"Didn't you always like the shawarma here?" Elan asked.

How could he remember that when she did not even remember? Elan. Damn you, Elan.

"Yes. The shawarma. That sounds great."

"And we'll have some pita and hummus. What do you think?" he asked.

"Sure. Yes. Hummus sounds good." She could hardly concentrate. Did she still love him after all these years, everything she'd been through, everything he'd done to her, and how he'd hurt her? Was that possible?

Elan placed the order and then looked at Katja and smiled.

"So, tell me, Kat, how are you? How have you been?" His voice was warm and deep with sincerity.

"I've been doing very well," she stammered. "My daughter just left two days ago. She was on leave from the IDF. The years pass so quickly, don't they? I can't believe she's all grown up."

"Yes, they certainly do. I remember when you were in the IDF, and I came to see you. Do you still remember that?"

"Of course, Elan. How could I ever forget?" Katja felt awkward. The memories were twisting her heart, and she felt like she might cry. "The army has been good for my daughter," she said, trying to change the subject.

"And you? Did you marry again after Mendel?"

"No, Elan. I never got married again after Mendel. I've devoted my time to building this organization for wives of fallen soldiers. I guess you could say it's given my life a purpose."

He smiled at her. "I understand. I was married to Noa's mother, but she passed away. And well, I never thought I could be married to anyone again."

"I am truly sorry about your wife."

"Yes, so am I. She was a wonderful woman."

"Noa is a sweet little girl, so I am sure her mother was a lovely person."

"Katja... You know, you're even more beautiful than you were twenty years ago."

She looked down at the tablecloth as she ran her fingers over her silverware.

"What do you want from me, Elan? Why did you ask me to come here with you?"

"Kat." He touched her hand.

She thought about pulling away. She was so emotionally confused, but his touch still sent electric shocks of desire through her. Damn him.

"I've missed you. It's hard for me to say this, very hard. I tried to tell you all these things once before, but my timing was terrible. It was right after Mendel was killed, but I don't think you were listening. Perhaps, maybe you do remember?"

She had no idea what he was talking about. She just shook her head. "I don't know what you're trying to tell me, Elan. I was in terrible shape after Mendel died. I had no idea how I was going to live without him."

"I tried to tell you all those years ago at Mendel's Shiva, and I want to say it again right now: I made a mistake when I broke our engagement. I was young, Kat. I was foolish. I loved you, but I couldn't cope with all the pressure I knew would be a part of marrying you because of your birth parents. I've realized now that I was so wrong. Can you forgive me?"

The food arrived. The smell of grilled chicken wafted through the air.

"Everything here is the same. Look, the chicken is cooked perfectly, just the way you like it, brown and crispy on the outside and sweet and moist on the inside." Elan smiled at her.

Katja returned his smile with a nervous smile of her own. Then she moved the salad and chicken around on her plate. Even now, she remembered how good the food was at this small café where she and Elan shared so many memories. But sitting across from him and reflecting, she'd lost her appetite. The candle on the table flickered, and it caught her eye. It was at that moment that she had a realization.

"Elan," she said, now sure of her words, now sure of her feelings. "I forgive you for everything that happened in the past. I understand how you could do what you did to me. I know you didn't mean to hurt me. You were just trying to do what you thought was right. You see, I understand because I did the same thing that you did to me, to someone whom I love."

"Then you'll consider giving us another try, Kat? Maybe we can start slowly, having dinner a few times a week."

Katja could hear the pleading in his voice, and she felt sorry for him. But in the last few minutes, all the magic of their past together dissipated like steam in the air. It was as if Katja had awakened from a long, troubled sleep. Her eyes were now open, and she was fully awake with a perfect understanding of all she had learned. And taking that knowledge, Katja knew what she must do.

She took a deep breath and put the fork down on the side of her plate. Then she looked directly into Elan's hopeful eyes.

"No, Elan. I'm sorry. I am really sorry, but what we had is a part of the past. There is nothing left."

It was so strange when Elan had first walked out on her. Katja had prayed for this day when he would come back, realizing how much he loved her. She'd created extensive fantasies in her mind of him begging her to come back. Sometimes, she would spurn him. Other times, she would allow herself to be taken into his arms and surrender to the passion.

But now that it had happened, all she felt was pity for him and a little sadness for what might have been. But the love, the desire, and the need were gone. "I guess our time has just passed. You will always have a special place in my heart. However, there is no going back for us. Not now, not anymore."

"But Katja, why? Why?"

"It's hard to explain. But now I understand why we are here together tonight. It is not to rekindle what we once had. It is God's way of showing me that I must not make the same mistake that you made with me. All I can do is hope that I am not too late…"

"But Kat?"

"I'm sorry, Elan."

Katja got up from the table, laying her napkin carefully on her plate. She walked over and kissed Elan's cheek. The book of love she'd kept open in her heart with Elan's name on the cover was now closed forever. Katja picked up her handbag and walked out of the restaurant and into the street.

CHAPTER SEVENTEEN

OUTSIDE THE CAFÉ, the wind whipped across Katja's face as she tried to hail a cab. Everything was clear to her now, clearer than it had ever been in her entire life. If only she weren't too late. The streetlight projected a golden halo as a taxi driver pulled to the side of the road, and she got inside the vehicle.

Traffic was beginning to lighten up. It was getting late, and the city was closing down. Katja had never been impatient, but she was now. She wanted to yell at the driver, to tell him to hurry. But of course, she couldn't. The cab was moving as fast as possible.

When Katja arrived at her house, she searched her handbag but could not find the card John had given her that day in the market. It was nowhere to be found. Panic began to set in. Pouring the contents of the bag onto the kitchen table, she riffled through it.

Tears of regret and frustration began to sting her eyes. Now that she was sure of what she wanted, she had no way of contacting John. It was like a light had gone on in her brain, and she was suddenly able to see the parallel between her relationship with Elan and her relationship with John. How could she have been so shallow? How could she have treated John the same way Elan treated her?

She needed to tell John what she felt, but she couldn't find the card and had no idea where to look for him. Angry at herself, Katja flung her purse on the floor. As the leather hit the marble, John's card fell silently out of a hole in the lining and onto the ground.

Katja's hand went to her throat. There it was—John's card. Trembling, she picked up the small piece of paper as if she'd just found a thousand gold bars. Then, with cold and trembling hands, she picked up the phone and dialed the number on the card. The receiver felt heavy in her hand. Ring—then another ring. It felt as if her nerves would shatter before she had a chance to speak. The phone rang five times before the answering machine picked up.

"You've reached the office of John Russell with the Levy and Klein Law Firm. If you are reaching this recording, Mr. Russell is either out of the office or is away from his desk. If you are calling between the hours of nine a.m. and five p.m., please dial zero and leave a message with the receptionist. Otherwise, wait for the tone and leave a voice message. Someone will return your call as soon as possible."

Of course, he wasn't in the office. How could she have thought he would be at work at ten in the evening?

"John, it's Katja," she said in a small voice, hoping with all her heart that she was not too late. "I just realized what time it is, so I am leaving a message. Please call me when you get this, John. It's important. I need to talk to you." She placed the telephone handset back on the cradle and sat down.

He might never call. What if he didn't? Could she find the courage to call again? Well, either way, it was doubtful that she would hear from him until morning. Dear God, a whole night to wait. She went into her bedroom, undressed, and got into bed but couldn't fall asleep. Her mind was ticking with thoughts, memories of Elan, memories of Mendel, and her father, too. But most of all, clarity: clarity about love, clarity about John.

At six in the morning, she finally gave up trying to sleep. The sun was peeking through the window and was about to make its entrance as the queen of the sky. Katja sat up on the bed, crossed her legs under her, and then looked outside. Out of the darkness of night, the brilliant sun, hot and golden, was beginning to illuminate her world. John. She whispered his name softly. It had been long since Katja had felt so sure of anything.

Two hours later, when Zofia began to make coffee, Katja came out of her room.

"Good morning, my sunshine," Zofia said. "I'm boiling water for coffee. Want a cup?"

Katja nodded.

"Mama, I need to talk to you."

"Of course. You can always talk to me. It's not that Elan again, is it? Did he do something terrible?"

"No, Mama, it's not Elan. Everything was fine with Elan. In fact, having dinner with Elan last night might have been the best thing I've ever done."

"*Oy vey*, Katja. You're not thinking about starting up with him again, are you? He hurt you so much, and I don't trust him."

"No, it's nothing like that. But it is something that you need to know. I am in love with someone. It is not Elan. It is a man I've known for a long time."

"And I don't know him? Who is it?" Zofia dried her hand on a dishcloth and sat across from her daughter.

"It's a long story. But he is a man I met a couple of years ago. We've been friends. We almost started a relationship, but I was a fool and broke it off."

"Because you were scared of getting hurt." Zofia nodded.

"Worse than that. I was scared of what people would say. Mama, he is a man of color. His skin is black."

"He is an Ethiopian Jew?"

"No, he's not a Jew at all. He's a Christian."

"Oh?" Zofia was a little taken aback.

"His name is John Russell. He is a lawyer, and well, he is the kindest, most understanding man I've ever met."

Zofia studied her daughter.

"Last night, when I was with Elan, I realized that I did the same thing to John that Elan did to me. I also realized that I made the biggest mistake of my life. I love John, and he loved me. I am just praying that he still loves me and will forgive me for being an idiot."

"You should call him and tell him how you feel," Zofia said.

"How do you feel about it, Mama?"

"I want you to be happy, Kat. I'm not going to live forever. I know you don't like to think about that, but it's true. When I go, it will comfort me to know that you have someone in your life who loves you and will take care of you."

"I tried to call him last night at work. Of course, his office was closed at ten p.m. I don't have his home number. I'm waiting for him to call me back. If he doesn't, I'll be devastated."

Zofia nodded.

"If he doesn't call, then I'll know I've lost him, the same way Elan knew last night that he'd lost me."

"Here, let me make you a cup of coffee," Zofia said.

Katja tried to stay busy, but the phone didn't ring the entire morning. Then, at ten o'clock, she heard the blessed sound of the ringing. Almost tripping over her own feet with her heart leaping like a frog in her chest, she picked up the receiver.

"Hello…"

"Kat? Where are you?"

Damn, it was Sarah Bloom, her new assistant at the organization.

"I'm sorry. I had some things to take care of this morning." Katja tried to hide the disappointment in her voice.

"You didn't tell me. I was expecting you an hour ago. I have some things I need to go over with you. By the way, we did very well with the fundraiser."

"Good, that's great," Katja said.

"Any idea what time I can expect you?"

"Give me an hour. I'll be in."

"Okay. Sounds good. Is it all right if I take a little extra time for lunch today? My sister is here from Haifa. She's only staying for the afternoon."

"Yes, yes, of course…"

Katja hung up the phone and felt as if she might cry. Zofia glanced over at her daughter but said nothing.

"It was Sarah Bloom. I am going to get dressed and go into the office," Katja said.

She walked slowly into the bathroom to take a shower. The thought of a day at work was almost unbearable. She wanted to get into bed, pull the covers over her head, and cry. But instead, she forced herself to get dressed. Katja had faced enough pain and disappointment in her time on earth to know that life goes on.

When Katja got out of the shower, she turned on the blow dryer to style her hair quickly. The sound muffled the knocking on the bathroom door for several minutes. But finally, she turned it off and heard Zofia.

"Katja, open the door."

Katja opened the door.

"He called while you were in the shower. He's waiting for you to call him back."

"Oh my God, Mama…"

Katja stood there in her robe, frozen to the ground, afraid to move, afraid to return the call, and afraid not to.

"Call him back," Zofia said, always the voice of logic.

Katja nodded and ran to the phone. She picked it up and dialed the number, biting her lower lip.

"This is John Russell."

"John, it's Katja."

CHAPTER EIGHTEEN

AFTER KATJA HAD WALKED out of the restaurant, leaving Elan alone
and rejected, he sat at the table for several minutes contemplating all
the mistakes he'd made in his life. Not everything was easily fixed.

When he'd gone on this date with Kat, he was sure she would
try again with him. Especially after she told him that she was not
married. He was disappointed. He'd been sure that he and Kat
could have a good life together, but now he had no choice but to
accept her decision. The waitress walked by the table. He flagged
her, took a pile of bills out of his pocket, and paid the check.

Elan walked through the streets of Tel Aviv. He'd had to park
two blocks away. Usually, he would have enjoyed the walk, but
tonight, he just wanted to get home. He finally got into his car. His
mind flashed back to the first time he and Katja had taken a road
trip to Jerusalem.

They had both been so young then, and everything in their lives
seemed as if it was going to be easy, sweet, and perfect. How arrogant he'd been then. He had thought that he was in complete
control of everything in his life.

Then that news about Katja came in like a sucker punch to the
stomach. It all happened so fast—the Nazi on trial in Israel and the

news about Katja and her birth mother. Everything had come as a shock, and he was repelled by the truth of Katja's birth parents. He couldn't imagine having children with her. He was stubborn then. Stubborn and unforgiving.

The automobile in front of him was going ten miles under the speed limit. He laid on his horn. "If you can't drive, you shouldn't be on the road, you imbecile," he said aloud, although no one else heard him. Elan pursed his lips. He felt empty, sad, and alone, but he wasn't sure if it was his heart that was hurting, his ego, or both.

Elan Amsel opened the door to his home. All was dark and peacefully quiet. He peeked into Noa's room. What a beautiful and sweet child she was. He shook his head. He'd almost messed things up with her, too. The only thing he'd ever gotten right in his life was Nina. Still, he could not help but blame himself for her death. After all, if he had not made her pregnant, she would not be gone.

Sweet Noa. She was the exchange God gave him for taking Nina. At first, he'd hated her, but now he had come to love her and vowed to protect her with his life. How he missed her mother. Noa was fast asleep. Quietly, Elan closed the door to her room. He was glad she was not awake because he was in a foul mood, and if she were awake, he'd have to pretend to be cheerful. It was hard for Elan to accept defeat in anything. He was standing in the hallway when he heard Gloria Finkelstein tiptoeing out of her room.

"Is there anything I can get for you, Mr. Amsel?"

"No, thanks."

"Then have a good night, sir." Gloria slipped back into her bedroom. The best thing about Mrs. Finkelstein was that she knew how to respect his privacy.

A bottle of bourbon caught his eye as he entered the living room. He'd left it half full on the coffee table. There was no need to bother with a glass. He would drink it right from the bottle. The room was dark, save for the moonlight. Elan unbuttoned his shirt and rubbed his well-toned belly. Then he flopped into the easy chair by the window and took a long, deep swig from the bottle. As always, the slight burn in his throat was a precursor to the relief from the emotional pain he needed to repress.

When he saw Katja at Noa's recital, she seemed so receptive that he let himself believe that there was a chance for the two of them. After losing Nina, he was sure he could never love anyone again. However, when he saw Katja, he was pulled back into the past, and his heart fluttered for the first time in years. He had not felt that way since Nina died, and Elan believed that perhaps he could be happy again by some miracle.

He hoped things would work out and he and Katja would marry. They were both older now; there would be no children, but she would have been able to give Noa the maternal guidance she needed.

Ah, but it was not to be. Elan thought if there was a God, he was punishing him for the terrible things he did in his younger years. Katja said that she had forgiven him, but she no longer loved him. That was worse than if she said she hated him. Forgiving him and no longer loving him made Elan feel pathetic. But how could he expect that she would ever love him after the way he treated her?

What a mess Elan had made of his life. Over the years, he'd made more enemies than friends. Most of the women he'd known despised him. In his office, his coworkers joked about his careless escapades with more women than he could count. In fact, his colleagues called him a cad. Of course, that was all before Nina. Now, he was known as a pathetic old man. Which was worse? He knew he drank too much and owed it to Noa to stop, but alcohol was the only thing that dulled the loneliness. Of course, he would never admit that to anyone—ever.

God, how he missed Nina. She was the only person who had ever really understood him. It was uncanny how she'd been able to see through his tough exterior to the soft underbelly he'd so carefully hidden beneath. "Nina," he whispered her name in the dark. "I'm trying, Nina. I'm trying to do the right thing by Noa." But he knew that he wasn't trying hard enough. If he were truly an alcoholic, he wouldn't be so functional at work. At least, that was what he kept telling himself. He felt so vulnerable, so exposed.

It was one thing when Katja rejected him right after he told her that Mendel had been killed. He'd expected her to be distraught and was not surprised that she was not open to his advances. But somewhere in the back of his mind, he'd believed that she would always love him. Now, he knew that whatever they had once shared was dead forever. Even though he'd not seen Katja in years, losing her love for him left a strange emptiness inside him. Little Noa was all he had in the world. He had tried to be a better person and a better father for her.

CHAPTER NINETEEN

Katja was holding the telephone receiver. It seemed like forever until John spoke.

"Kat. Oh, my God. I was praying that you would call."

Her hand trembled so hard that she could barely hold the handset. She cleared her throat, and then she said, "John, I know this sounds crazy, but I had a revelation last night."

"Nothing is crazy, Kat—nothing."

"I realized I've spent my entire life trying to please everyone else. I was always trying to fit in, to do what other people thought I should do so that they wouldn't see the damage inside of me—so they wouldn't see my faults. I wanted everyone to like me, so I became what they wanted me to be, no matter what that was.

"But it was not like that with you, John. With you, I laid my soul bare, and you saw me as I really am. Then something amazing happened. You loved me anyway. You didn't care who my real parents were or whether I was born in a hellhole built by the Nazis to breed their special children. You loved me. You never judged me, John. I'm tired of living for everyone else. When I was with you, it was the first time I've felt truly happy since Mendel died."

"I don't know what to say," his voice breaking, "except that you've just made me happier than I ever thought possible. And yes, Kat, you're right. I would never judge you for anything. You're a beautiful, kind, and giving person. In fact, you've devoted your life to the service of others…"

"I love you, John. I don't care what people say or what they think. I love you. I'm willing to stand up to the world and announce that you are the man I've chosen to marry. I don't care what color your skin is. To me, you are perfect and beautiful just the way you are. You could be green for all I care. I love you. I love your heart, I love your mind, and I love the way you make me see the good in myself."

"Am I dreaming? Oh, Kat. You are so right. I see so much good in you, and I do love you. I can't say it enough. It won't be easy for us, but I'm willing to face whatever hurtful, prejudiced crap the world throws at us just to be with you. Marry me? God, Kat, I've loved you for years."

"Yes. Yes. Yes!" She was crying and laughing at the same time, but most of all, she was sure. She was sure that she had made the right decision.

CHAPTER TWENTY

February's weather in Chicago is brutal. The morning that Bari Lynn Allen and her best friend Marilyn arrived at the O'Hare Airport was no exception. Although there had not been a snowfall for several days, the frigid temperatures had dropped to fifteen degrees Fahrenheit.

The entire collection of congregants from Temple Beth Israel met at gate D12. They were buzzing with excitement. Today was the day they'd all been waiting for—they would board a direct flight from Chicago to Israel.

Once they landed at their destination, the plan was that they would separate into two groups. The adults from Beth Israel would tour together, and the young adults would tour the country separately from their parents. The teenagers would hike through the mountains and climb Masada, activities that might be too strenuous for most of the older members.

Eight months earlier, a travel agency that had worked with the synagogue in the past was called to send an agent to the temple to meet with the rabbi to plan the tour for the congregants.

The person who arrived was a short elf of a girl with a smile bigger than her face and protruding ears that popped out of the sides of her short pixie haircut. Her petite frame was neatly dressed in a navy-blue skirt and a white blouse. She exuded confidence and appeared to be very organized. In her left hand, she carried a folder that contained a pile of neatly arranged papers.

"Hi, you must be Rabbi Goodman?"

"Yes, and you're Shirley Douglas from the travel agency?"

"I am. It's a pleasure to meet you."

The Rabbi had many questions, which Shirley promptly answered. But most importantly, he was concerned with the safety of the members of his shul. Shirley Douglas assured the rabbi that the group would be as safe as possible.

"Of course," Shirley said. "Israel is a dangerous place. But you must already know that. There are sometimes bombings in restaurants, hotels, or buses. No one has control over such things. But I guarantee you that I will do my best. I can arrange with the Israeli Ministry of Tourism to have several members of the IDF tour with the teenagers and keep an eye on them. Sometimes, kids stray from the group, and in Israel, that can be unsafe. The adults will be fine with a tour guide."

"Yes, that is a very good idea. Contact the Ministry and ask for a group of IDF soldiers to watch over the teenagers. Miss Douglas, please do everything possible to ensure our members come home safely."

"I promise, Rabbi Goodman. I will."

The mood of the passengers on the plane was charged with excitement. They were talking and laughing. Some of the older people had brought food, although the airlines offered plenty. Temple Beth Israel was a Reform synagogue, so most members did not keep kosher. Everyone onboard was high on the idea that they were on their way to Israel, to the Jewish homeland. The Promised Land.

But for Bari Lynn, this trip had many objectives. It was a vacation away from her overbearing mother. Spending time with her best friend on a trip to a foreign land was fun and exciting.

But for Bari, this was also a mission to find her father, the father she had spent her entire life believing was an American who died in the Vietnam War. Who was this man who had spawned her? Why had he abandoned her and her mother? It was hard for her to believe that her father was an Israeli.

The news had come as quite a shock. Now that she knew her father was alive, she had to know more about him. She had to know everything. As the airliner swept away from America, its sleek body stealing through the white clouds, Bari Lynn whispered her father's name to herself so that no one else could hear. Elan Amsel. Who are you, Elan Amsel? Elan Amsel…

THE RUNWAY AT BEN GURION AIRPORT, TEL AVIV, ISRAEL;
FEBRUARY 1986

Marilyn, who was sitting beside Bari Lynn, squeezed Bari Lynn's hand as the plane gently came to a stop… "As a spokesperson for the State of Israel, I would like to welcome all of you to our homeland," the pilot said over the loudspeaker.

"The temperature outside today is a comfortable sixty-five degrees Fahrenheit. Please enjoy your stay with us."

"Can you believe we're here? We're in Israel," Marilyn said, craning her neck to look out the window. "I'm so excited."

"Me too…" Bari Lynn giggled. For the first time in her life, Bari Lynn felt independent, courageous, and even pretty.

As soon as the plane had left Chicago, and she was away from her mother's scrutinizing gaze, Bari went into the bathroom on the plane and changed her clothes. She'd put on some things she'd borrowed from Marilyn. They were stylish, and for once, she felt someone might even find her sexy. Bari wore a black tee shirt with the collar cut out so that it hung off one of her pale shoulders and tight jeans.

The night before they left, Marilyn had used an actual clothing iron on Bari's hair and had managed to get it perfectly straight. During the thirteen-hour flight, Marilyn had carefully glamorized Bari's appearance with the magic tools in her cosmetic bag. With just a little eyeliner, a little mascara, and wine-colored lipstick, suddenly Bari was transformed. Marilyn cocked her head and smiled. "You look amazing!"

"Give me the mirror. I want to see," Bari said.

"Nope, not until we're in Israel. I don't want you to have a chance to get cold feet and wash all the makeup off."

Then, as soon as the pilot announced they were landing, Marilyn handed Bari her compact with the mirror inside. Bari stared at the alluring image, and she hardly knew herself. The shy, awkward girl she'd always been had disappeared, leaving a very attractive, confident woman in her place.

As they followed the line of passengers out of the aircraft and into Ben Gurion National Airport, Bari Lynn's heart was beating fast. She and Marilyn were best friends. Bari felt that she could share anything with her. So, Marilyn was the only person she'd ever told the truth about her father. The night before they left Chicago, the two girls had gone out for french fries and cokes. They sat in a booth in a small diner not far from their homes. Bari took a few sips of her Coke.

"Mar, I have something to tell you," Bari said. "My father is alive…"

"What? I thought he died in Vietnam."

"So did I, but he didn't. I found out the truth last night. My dad, I mean Lucas, my stepdad, told me everything. My birth father's name is Elan Amsel. Believe it or not, he lives somewhere in Israel. I don't know if he knows about me or not… I don't know anything about him except that I want to see him. I want to talk to him and ask him some questions."

Together, Bari and Marilyn had devised a plan to find Bari's father. They decided that first, they would look up his name in the phone book, and once they found his number, they would sneak down to the lobby of one of the hotels and call him when everyone was asleep. Marilyn agreed that it was Bari's right to know her birth father, even though she was afraid that facing Elan Amsel might end up hurting Bari more than helping her. But Bari begged Marilyn to do this with her, and Marilyn agreed. After all, they were best friends, and they would find him together.

As Bari and Marilyn pulled their luggage off the revolving conveyor belt, they saw several of the older people who had come with the synagogue kneeling and kissing the ground.

"That's weird," Bari said.

"Yep, I'm really glad my father couldn't get away from work, or my parents might be here doing the same thing. I'm so glad they're at home. I'm free!" Marilyn shouted.

"We're both free!" Bari exclaimed.

Both girls laughed, and then they began to follow the rest of the group.

They walked a few feet until they saw a group of five people, two women and three men, all wearing IDF uniforms. The two women held a sign that said, "Welcome to Israel, Congregation Beth Israel young adults." One of the men from the IDF was playing a guitar, and all the Israeli soldiers were singing a welcome song in Hebrew.

Bari Lynn nudged Marilyn. "Look at the one playing the guitar. He is so sexy. I put dibs on him."

"You're right, he is really good-looking, and his voice just melts me. Can you see his name tag?"

"Yeah. It looks like it says, Ido."

"Ido?" Marilyn asked.

"It's an Israeli name, I guess," Bari Lynn said. "Well, he is just too much with those dark eyes and that deep voice. Hell, I'm finally away from my mother, and I can do whatever I want. So, I don't care what his name is. I've decided right here and now, whatever it takes; he's gonna be mine, my first guy."

"You mean the first guy you do it with? Really, Bari? You're gonna sleep with him?"

"Yep," Bari Lynn said. "I am."

"Oh, Bari, are you sure?"

"Yep, what better time and place to lose it? I mean, I'm far away from my mom. I feel bold. I feel confident. Plus, we're in a different country, and nobody knows me here. I can be whoever I want to be." She giggled. "I feel like I am ready to spread my wings and fly." Marilyn laughed, too. Then Bari said, "It just feels so good to have finally escaped from my mom's clutches. Finally."

Both girls looked at each other and smiled.

A male voice came over the loudspeaker. He was saying something in Hebrew. Everyone at the Ben Gurion Airport seemed to come to a complete halt. If an outsider had been watching, they would have thought every person in the entire building was playing the childhood game of freeze frame. But, of course, this was no game.

Bari looked at Marilyn and grabbed her hand. The old childhood fears that had been instilled in Bari came rising from her gut like the lava of a volcano. The words of warning she'd grown up hearing from her mother blasted through her mind. She was once again reminded of the dangers that she'd been taught lurked around every corner. "What did he say?" Bari asked Marilyn. Bari's body was trembling.

"I have no idea. I don't speak Hebrew well enough to understand." Marilyn squeezed Bari's hand.

Then, the man on the loudspeaker repeated his words, this time in English:

"Attention, your attention, please. We would like to inform you that the notorious Nazi, John Demjanjuk, also known as 'Ivan the Terrible,' at the Treblinka Concentration Camp, where he committed crimes against humanity, has just arrived in Israel. At this moment, he is being escorted to prison. He will stand trial here in our Jewish homeland for the atrocities he committed against the Jews and many other innocent people. It has been a long time that he has been able to live as a free man, but justice will finally be done. Shalom."

Across the aisle, two casually dressed, non-distinct males stood huddled together against the wall of the building. They were diagonal to the walkway where the group of American young adults who had just arrived from Chicago were now surrounding the members of the IDF. These two men had made sure that they were hidden by the crowds of people from the view of the Israeli soldiers.

"That's them. They're here," one of the men said to the other.

"Yes, I know. I read the sign. It said, 'Welcome, Congregation Beth Israel.' It was written in English, of course."

"Of course, your English is impeccable due to that Harvard education you got in the United States." The first man whispered to the other so that he could not be heard by any passersby.

"Yes, and while I studied in America, I had the opportunity to meet and get to know some of the people. It amazed me to find out just how naïve and trusting the Americans are, especially the young ones."

Both men barked a laugh in unison.

"What an opportunity has fallen right into our laps. Just look over there: an entire group of Jewish–American teenagers and young adults right here in Israel. We should take two girls. Israel may not negotiate with us, but they will have to bend to American pressure. This is perfect!

"Because they are young Jewish–Americans, whatever happens to them will attract media attention in every country. Americans have weak stomachs when it comes to their women. We need that kind of strong attention to make our point. Remember how the U.S. condemned the Israeli attack on Iran's nuclear reactor and how they were not pleased with them during the Lebanese War? More than once, Israel has been rebuked for using weapons the Americans gave them for defensive purposes only to attack Arabs aggressively.

"Even if we fail and have to kill the girls, it will still help our cause. It will drive a wedge between Israel and America. These stupid children will help us make the world shake with fear..."

CHAPTER TWENTY-ONE

THAT NIGHT, the American teenagers met with their IDF tour guides in the lobby of the hotel where they were staying. The guides introduced themselves.

"Thank God they're wearing name tags," Marilyn whispered to Bari, "or I'd never remember their names."

"Yeah, the Israeli names are different. But I wouldn't forget Ido, that's for sure."

"Okay, so let's go over this. There is Ido, the one you think is so sexy."

Bari Lynn giggled. "Then there is Jordan. That's the other guy with the group."

"Yeah, his name is easy, but the girls… Ima, Adina, and Hila are kind of strange and hard to remember."

"Not really so bad," Bari Lynn said, "but I am glad they're wearing name tags."

"Yeah…" Marilyn laughed.

After the meeting, everyone was served small pastries and instant coffee. Bari Lynn tried to look fetching to get Ido's attention, but he seemed too busy with the group to notice her. Everyone from the temple was excited as Jordan went over the itinerary that was planned for them.

"Everyone. Your attention please, come on now, all of you, be quiet. I have some things to tell you… In case you've forgotten, my name is Jordan. My friends and I will be your guides for the next ten days.

"We would like to welcome all of you to Israel. This is our home, and since you are Jews, it is your homeland, too. I speak for all the soldiers who are here today, Ima, Ido, Adina, Hila, and myself, when I say that our greatest wish for you is that by the time you return home, you have come to love Israel as much as we do," Jordan said.

The four other soldiers clapped their hands.

After the clapping had stopped, Jordon began again. "Now, this is very important, so please listen closely. You must never stray from the group. Do you understand? If you can't see one of the IDF members, then you have gone out of the range of our protection. We will tell you where it is safe for you to go.

"Don't worry; there will be plenty of shops and things for you to see on the Israeli side of Israel. You'll have plenty to do. There is nothing to fear as long as you follow our directions. You are perfectly safe, but be sure that you do not stray."

"I think Ido smiled at me," Bari Lynn whispered in Marilyn's ear.

"I know. I thought I saw that, too."

"I'm going to try to talk to him," Bari Lynn said.

She tried, but it was impossible to get Ido alone. He was surrounded by American teenagers with questions, as were the other Israelis. Finally, it was getting late, and they were planning to get an early start in the morning, so everyone went to their rooms.

There were two other girls sharing the hotel room with Bari and Marilyn, so Bari found it difficult to talk to Marilyn privately. She was frustrated. She wanted advice on how to get Ido's attention, but she told herself that they had only just arrived that afternoon. She would have plenty of time to get closer to Ido.

The following morning, the group was expected to meet in a

designated meeting room downstairs in the hotel lobby, where they would be served breakfast. Marilyn helped Bari to apply her makeup, and then the two went downstairs. The Israelis were waiting, but so were several of the other Americans.

A buffet table was set up with hummus, fresh green pepper, persimmons, boiled eggs, fresh olives, and pita.

"This is kind of strange for breakfast," Marilyn said. "It's a little nauseating first thing in the morning."

"Yeah, but I expected the customs to be different. Didn't you?"

"Yes, I did, but now I wish I had cereal and milk." Marilyn made a face.

Bari Lynn laughed. She took a hard-boiled egg and two triangles of pita bread. Marilyn followed her lead, and then they sat at one of the long tables.

The Americans were shuffling in slowly. Then, to Bari's shock and delight, Ido sat beside her. It should not have come as a surprise. All the Israelis were trying to make personal contact with their American guests. They wanted to be sure the guests were comfortable and had everything they needed.

"Hi, I'm Ido."

Bari Lynn looked at Marilyn, and her eyes got wide. Marilyn knew her friend was at a loss for words, so she took over.

"I'm Marilyn, and this is Bari Lynn."

"Hi," Bari Lynn said.

"You girls like to shop? I'm sure you do. I've heard most American women love shopping," Ido smiled.

"Oh, yeah!" Marilyn said. "We love it! In fact, we spend every weekend at the mall when we're at home."

"Then today is going to be a lot of fun for you. You'll love the shopping here in Tel Aviv. Then later this afternoon, when it cools off, we'll go to the beach."

Bari Lynn felt uncomfortable. She wasn't sure she wanted to be seen in a bathing suit. She cringed as she thought about her body. It was so pasty white and unattractive. Although she was no longer overweight, Bari Lynn still felt like she was fat. She saw a fat girl with frizzy red hair and freckles whenever she looked at herself in the mirror.

Marilyn had straightened her hair and added more brown to the color. Even though she wore makeup to cover her freckles, lost weight, and toned her body, Bari didn't see herself that way. She still lacked confidence. A bathing suit! She hadn't even brought one with her, but of course, she was sure Marilyn had several. Bari looked at the Israeli girls and felt inferior in comparison because they were very tan and fit.

"You'll love the beach here."

Bari Lynn smiled an uncomfortable smile.

Ido had a natural radar for detecting distressed minds. This radar had been the force that saved many troubled young people who were drafted into the IDF. It also made him an expert in dealing with difficult cases and the person to consult when a recruit needed extra attention. When Ido felt the nervousness coming from Bari Lynn, he decided to try harder to help her relax and feel at home. He could easily see that she was an introvert, clumsy, and afraid of ridicule.

"I haven't been to the beach in years," Bari said.

"All the more reason to go," Ido smiled. "We'll have a volleyball game. It will be fun."

Bari Lynn smiled. She loved his eyes. They were dark and sincere, and they made her feel as if he would accept her no matter what she looked like without her clothes. She was so tired of being a baby. At eighteen, she was the only one of her friends who had never been to bed with a boy. But it was hard to grow up with her mother hovering over her.

Bari longed to grow up, to be a part of things instead of always being an outsider. It was irrational, but she only had fourteen days before she returned to Chicago and fell back under her mother's control. There was no time to waste. If Ido was the one she wanted to lose her virginity to, she'd better hurry up and give him some signs. The problem was, she had no idea how to flirt. She'd always been too shy and self-conscious. Bari Lynn had to think of something.

"You're going to love Israel. It's a wonderful country," Ido said.

"Yeah, Marilyn and I are really excited to be here."

"Well, we are glad to have you. After all, you are our American cousins. Did you know that because you are Jewish, you are automatically Israeli citizens?"

"Yeah, I heard that, but I wasn't sure if it was true," Bari Lynn said.

"It is true," he said, smiling. "This is as much your homeland as it is ours."

Ido's smile and the soft caress of his voice made Bari Lynn feel as if she'd been embraced. All of her life, she'd wanted to be a part of the popular group, the cool kids who had boyfriends and were loved. Ido made her feel wanted.

"Everyone, may I have your attention?" Hila said, speaking through a microphone so the crowd of excited teenagers could hear her over the chatter. "Quiet down for a minute." She waited until the hum ceased. "Now listen. We are going shopping in Tel Aviv today. Again, I want to remind you to please stay with the group. Always make sure that you can see one of us at all times. If you can't, then you've gone too far. All right? Now let's go and have some fun…"

The morning was spent shopping in Tel Aviv. Bari bought silver rings for her mother and father. In a small boutique shop, she purchased a hand-painted seder plate for her grandmother. They went into a jewelry store famous for Israeli silver. Marilyn found a Star of David necklace for her grandmother.

Outside the shops, they were always able to see at least one of the Israelis from their group. No matter which way they went within the designated area, Ido, Ima, Hila, Adiana, or Jordon leaned against a building with a cigarette or talked to one of the Americans. After a full morning of walking, exploring, and purchasing, the girls realized they were starving. Bari and Marilyn stopped at a crowded restaurant for lunch.

"Breakfast was really yucky," Marilyn said. "I am so hungry. I hope lunch will be better."

"Yeah, me too. I knew the food would be different than we were used to, so I was expecting it."

"Yeah, but cold vegetables in the morning. And the coffee, it was like instant coffee, not real coffee. Yuck."

"I know. But come on Mar, we didn't come here to eat. We came here to see Israel."

"Yeah, and more importantly, you came to get away from your mother."

"That's for sure. And…"

"And?"

"To meet the man who made my mom pregnant."

"Oh yeah, that. You don't call him your father."

"That's because he's not. Lucas is my real father. He was just like… there, if you know what I mean."

"Then why the hell do you want to find him?"

"I don't know. I guess to see what kind of man he is and to ask him why he abandoned my mom."

"You sound a little bitter about the whole thing."

"Yeah, maybe I am. But in a way, I'm glad. I couldn't have had a better father than Lucas. He was not only a great dad, but he has always been a great friend. I guess I want to find this Elan Amsel guy more out of curiosity than anything else. It's confusing. I guess once I meet him, I'll be able to put it all to rest."

The menu was in Hebrew, but the waiter spoke English. Marilyn told him she wanted *something American*. He laughed and said he was sorry for laughing at her, but he had heard that before from American visitors. Then he made some suggestions about things he thought they might like. The two girls agreed with his ideas and ordered their food.

"I think Ido likes you," Marilyn said.

"I hope so. But how can you tell?"

"I don't know. He looks at you differently than he looks at the rest of us."

"Really?" Bari Lynn blushed. "Are you sure? Oh my God, I like him so much!"

"Yeah… I think so. Kinda like he takes a special interest in you. You know guys can tell when you like them."

"You think he can tell how I feel?" Bari Lynn was embarrassed but excited.

"I think so. You've been giving him *come-on* looks since we got here. He can see that. He's not blind, Bari."

Bari Lynn giggled. She wanted to believe Ido liked her, but she couldn't be sure. "What should I do next?"

"I don't know. What do you want to do?"

"Come on, Mar, I told you what I want to do."

"Okay, okay. Listen, I have an idea. When we are playing volleyball today, why don't you say you feel sick and ask him to escort you back to the hotel so you don't get lost? Then you know…"

"What? Then what?"

Marilyn laughed. "You know…"

"The problem is, I don't know, Mar."

"Okay. Listen, silly. I'll tell you what to do…"

CHAPTER TWENTY-TWO

BARI LYNN SLIPPED into her bathing suit and frowned at the reflection in the mirror. She was as white as the walls in the hotel room.

"I look awful," Bari said to Marilyn.

"No, you don't. You look fine."

"I'm going to put on shorts. That way, my white legs won't stand out so much."

Bari Lynn pulled on her denim shorts and wrapped her long auburn hair into a high ponytail. Marilyn touched up Bari's makeup, and then Bari looked in the mirror again.

"It's the best I can do…" She flung her arms up.

"You look fine, Bari. Stop worrying. Okay?"

Bari Lynn nodded, but she couldn't help but glance back at the mirror again. Gee, she really wished she were a prettier girl. If only she were beautiful, Ido would fall at her feet because men were visually oriented.

All the teenagers had begun climbing the stairs to the bus that was to take them to the beach. They carried towels from the hotel and bottles of sunscreen. Ido jumped the stairs onto the bus in one motion. Then he waved to the rest of the group. He looked amazing in his bathing suit. His tan, muscular body glistened with sweat, and Bari felt herself swoon.

When they got to the beach, Ido and Jordan set up the volleyball net while the rest of the soldiers talked to the teenagers. Marilyn and Bari stood off to the side by themselves.

"The Israeli girls are totally beautiful," Bari said, "especially Ima."

"You mean the IDF soldiers?"

"Yes, of course, I mean the soldiers," Bari said, annoyed.

"Ima doesn't even look Israeli. She's so blond and light-skinned. And those eyes... I wonder if they are really that blue or if she is wearing contact lenses?"

"She's gorgeous. She looks like a model," Bari said. Then, she turned away from the group and huddled against Marilyn. "I don't think I can do this."

"You mean, ask Ido back to the room?"

"Yeah. I feel so ugly."

"You're not ugly."

"I don't know. I think I am."

"Bari, this is your chance. Before you know it, the trip will be over, and we'll be back in Chicago. Take advantage of our time here, your time of freedom from your mom."

"You're right. I have to. I have to stop being so scared and just do it."

The volleyball game began. They played for almost a half hour before Ido took a break, and one of the others went in to take his place. He was standing on the sidelines, watching. Bari had not yet been in the game, so she, too, was on the sidelines. Marilyn caught Bari's gaze and fixed her stare on her. Without speaking, Marilyn mouthed the words, "Do it now. Go over and tell him you're feeling sick."

Bari took a deep breath and contorted her face. Marilyn smiled and mouthed the words, "Go on."

Bari nodded. She was trembling as she walked over to Ido.

"Can I speak to you for a minute?" she asked.

"Sure." He walked far enough away from the crowd for her to feel comfortable that their conversation would be private.

"I don't feel well. Will you please take me back to the hotel?"

"Yes, of course," Ido said. "Give me a minute to tell the others."

Ido walked over to the rest of the IDF soldiers to explain the situation. As soon as Ido turned his back, Bari Lynn nodded at Marilyn, and Marilyn nodded back and smiled.

There was no method of transportation other than the huge bus, so Ido drove, and Bari sat in the first row across from him.

"How do you feel?" he asked.

"Not great," she said. It was true, but she wasn't sick, she was nervous.

When they got back to the hotel, Ido asked Bari if she wanted something to drink.

"Yes, that would be great."

"Come, let's go and sit in the coffee shop, and we'll get you something cold to drink."

Bari nodded.

They sat down and ordered. Bari had never been on a date, and this felt the closest she'd ever come. Of course, she knew it wasn't a real date, but it felt good to pretend.

Bari sat in the booth across from Ido, quietly sipping on her cola. She was at a loss for words.

"Is this the first time you've been away from home?" Ido asked.

"Yeah, how did you know? Does it show that badly?"

"Let's just say I have a knack for knowing these things." He smiled. "I've worked with new recruits in the IDF long enough that I can tell."

If someone else had asked her that, Bari would have been offended. She would have felt that she was being judged. But Ido made her feel special. With him, she felt accepted and strangely warm all over.

"Well, you hit the point with me. It's my first time away without my parents."

"I'll bet it was hard for you to leave home. You seem to me to be a daddy's girl."

She laughed. "I am. Wow, you're, like, psychic. I love my step-dad. He's always been my best friend. My mom? Now that's another story."

"She's tough on you?"

"That's an understatement. In fact, can you keep a secret?" She suddenly felt the need to confide in him.

"Sure. Secrets are my specialty," he smiled.

"I didn't even know my real dad was alive until a few months before I left for this trip. You see, my mom lied to me. Can you imagine? She lied to me for my whole life. She told me my birth father was killed in the Vietnam War.

"But a few months ago, I found out that my father is an Israeli. My mother was married and divorced in Israel when she was young. It was a real shock to learn that my father might be alive. I looked up his name in the phone book but couldn't find him. I'm going to try in every city that we visit. I would really like to talk to him. I have a lot of questions I'd like to ask him."

"What's his name? Maybe I can make some inquiries for you."

"You won't tell anyone why you are looking for him, will you?"

"Not if you don't want me to."

"I don't, at least not until I talk to him first."

"I understand."

"His name is Elan Amsel. If you can help me find him, that would be really helpful…"

"I'll do what I can."

Marilyn told Bari that no man would ever turn down sex. In fact, Marilyn had given her specific instructions on what to do when she was alone with Ido. Marilyn said if Bari did as she said, it would be easy to seduce Ido. It was not easy for Bari to act the part of a *femme fatale*. In fact, as she tried to talk to Ido, the words stuck in her throat. There was so much about him that she liked and trusted. But how could she possibly offer herself to him without dying of embarrassment? Just do it, Bari. Just say the words Marilyn told you to say.

Bari toyed with the straw in her cola glass.

"Are you feeling any better?" Ido asked.

"Yes, much better. Thank you."

"I'm glad. The heat must have been too much for you."

"Ido…"

He cocked his head to listen.

"When do you think everyone will be back from the beach?"

"Let's see, it's two o'clock. I think maybe five o'clock or so. You can go upstairs and take a nap. I'll stay in the hotel until a quarter to five or so, and then I'll take the bus back to the beach and pick up the rest of the group."

Okay, this was the chance she'd been waiting for. Just say it, Bari. She squeezed her eyes shut. Looking down at the table, she said, "Why don't you come up to my hotel room? I really like you and, well… I haven't done this before, so I am not sure what else to say."

"Oh…" Ido said. Then he bopped himself in the forehead with the heel of his hand as if he had just realized he'd done something stupid. "Bari, I am so sorry. This is all my fault. I think I might have given you the wrong impression." What was he thinking?

He was just trying to help her to come out of her shell, but of course, he gave her the wrong impression. Ido knew how important his choice of words was right now. Her ego was fragile. He could see by looking at her that she lacked confidence. "I think you are a beautiful girl. I'm very flattered, but I am a happily married man. Ima, the other soldier, who is with us, the one with the blonde hair, she is my wife."

Bari felt humiliated. All she could do was shrug her shoulders and shake her head—she couldn't speak.

"Bari, it's okay. Don't feel bad. If I was a single guy, I would jump at the chance to be with a girl as pretty as you…" Ido said.

Her fingers were trembling as she touched the straw in her glass. Bari wanted to get out of there, to be away from Ido, before she started crying, and the last thing she wanted was to cry in front of him. It was too hard to speak. She was afraid he would hear the pain in her voice. So, Bari Lynn got up from the table and ran through the lobby to the elevator, which had just stopped.

When the elevator doors opened, an old woman with gray hair rinsed with a purple stain got out. Bari jumped in and pressed the button to her floor just as she saw Ido coming towards her. The elevator door closed, and Bari started to cry.

Ido was angry with himself. How could he have been so stupid? He should have mentioned that he was married right away so that Bari wouldn't have put her ego on the line like that. Now, he had a heartbroken American teenager who would be uncomfortable in his presence.

As soon as he was able to speak to the other soldiers, he would see to it that one of the others kept an eye on Bari and her girl-friend. It was probably better if he stayed away from her. Ido felt terrible. His main goal in making the connection with Bari was to help her to feel accepted, and it had backfired on him. And now, with how she behaved, he dared not leave her alone in the hotel. It was the job of the IDF soldiers to guarantee that these kids got home safely.

Ido would have sat in the lobby the entire afternoon if it were up to him. But he had to return the bus to the beach so the rest of the group would have transportation back. He doubted Bari would leave her room, but he couldn't be sure. Bari's ego was bruised, and Ido knew she would not want to see him now. She probably would need the support of her best friend before she was able to face him.

Ido's innate sense of human nature assured him that Bari would stay as far away from him for the rest of the trip as possible. Still, just to be safe, he would ask the desk clerk to keep an eye out for Bari. If she was foolish enough to try to leave the hotel on her own, the clerk was to call the local police immediately. Ido planned to return to the bus and have one of the other soldiers drive him back to the lobby. It would not take more than a half hour before he returned. But just in case there was a problem, Ido wrote down the location of the beach where the police could find the group if neces-sary and gave it to the man at the front desk.

"Keep an eye out for the girl. Did you see her with me when we came in?"

"Yes."

"You remember what she looks like? Dark reddish-brown hair?"

"I remember her exactly."

"Good. I will be back as quickly as I can," Ido said.

Bari Lynn was mortified. She'd made a fool of herself, and now she would have to see Ido every day for the rest of this trip. There was no way to leave early. Besides, she wouldn't do that to Marilyn, even though she was blaming Marilyn for encouraging her to make a fool of herself right now.

A sick feeling in the pit of her stomach nagged at her. She was alone in the hotel room as she took off her shorts and stood in the bathing suit she'd purchased at the hotel gift shop. Scrunching up her forehead and frowning, she looked at herself in the mirror. Her breasts were too small, but she had to admit she wasn't flabby. Thank God for the martial arts that Lucas had taught her. At least she wasn't fat anymore.

When she was young, she was fat. That was a terrible time in her life. People had made her life miserable when she was over-weight. Now, whenever Bari spotted a heavyset girl on the street, Bari's heart went out to her. Bari hated her sensitivity because she could easily feel and relate to other people's pain, and the problem was that often, she took it on as her own.

Frowning, Bari Lynn scrutinized every part of her body. Her skin was so pale and chalky. Next to Ido's Israeli wife, she looked sickly. And wouldn't Ido have to be married to the prettiest of the Israeli soldiers? To Bari, Ima looked as if she'd lead a charmed life. She had probably been popular and had her choice of men, not like Bari, a girl nobody wanted. And although makeup covered the freckles on Bari's nose, she still had a sprinkling across her cream-colored chest.

It had taken two hours, but Marilyn had tamed her curly hair with an iron, and now it laid straight down her back. As long as her hair didn't get wet, she would be all right. But like Cinderella at midnight, if water touched Bari's hair, it would turn back into a frizzy mess.

Friends of Bari's parents said she was cute. Of course, they were family friends. What were they going to say, that she was ugly? Bari studied herself in the mirror. Why did some girls have it so easy while she had to work hard to be considered somewhat attractive?

No matter what she did, Bari knew she was not beautiful. She would never be beautiful, not like Ima, not like Ido's wife.

Bari flung herself on the bed and began to condemn herself with a barrage of self-hatred and criticism. Why would she think a guy like Ido would even want to go out with her? She was stupid— ugly and stupid.

She wished she could call her stepfather. Lucas would know what to say. If she could only talk to him, he would find the right words to make it possible for her to face Ido again. But she knew she couldn't call Chicago. There was nothing to do but lie there and wait for Marilyn to return to the room.

When the other four girls, Marilynn included, returned from the beach, they gathered around Bari Lynn.

"How are you feeling?" one of the girls asked, putting her hand on Bari's forehead.

"Everyone was worried about you…"

"I'm fine. I'm doing much better. Thanks for your concern," Bari said, a little too curt. She wanted them all to go away so she could talk to Marilyn alone.

"Are you going to come down to dinner?"

"No, I'm not feeling well enough to eat yet," Bari said, hoping that when the others went down for dinner, she and Marilyn could have a private conversation.

"Can I bring something up for you? Maybe you'll want to eat later?" one of the others asked.

"No, thanks. Really, I appreciate it, but I'll be okay." Bari forced a smile.

After they showered and got dressed, the others went down for dinner. Bari and Marilyn stayed in the room.

"What the hell happened?" Marilyn asked.

"He's married to Ima."

"The pretty one?"

"Yeah, of course. Of course, it would have to be the pretty one."

"Hey, Bari, you're pretty, too."

"No, not really. With a hell of a lot of work, I'm okay. Not really pretty, just okay."

"Bari," Marilyn said, touching her back.

"Let's face it. I wasn't blessed with great beauty, a great personality, or anything…"

For a few minutes, Marilyn rubbed Bari's back.

"Listen, I have an idea. While everyone else is at dinner, let's go out and have some fun. We can sneak out of the hotel and check out some of the bars here in Tel Aviv. I've heard that they won't card us. We can get away with ordering drinks. I think when some cute guys hit on you, you'll realize that you really are pretty," Marilyn said, smiling.

"Do you think we'll get caught?" Bari Lynn asked.

"Nah. Everyone is going out as a group tonight. They won't be back until late. We can stuff our bed with pillows and then cover them so it looks like we're sleeping. When the other girls get back to the room, they'll be too tired to try to wake us. Then we'll be back in our beds before morning. Nobody will know that we ever left."

"Okay."

"Hurry up. Let's get ready. I want to get out of here as soon as they leave."

"What time did they say the bus was leaving the hotel?"

"Seven."

"So far, every time the bus goes somewhere, it always leaves at least fifteen minutes late. I guess it takes that long to get everyone together. Let's wait until we're sure they are gone, and then we can sneak out at about seven thirty," Bari said.

CHAPTER TWENTY-THREE

GERHARD HELMUT STRETCHED out his long, gangly legs. It had been a stressful flight for him from Germany to Israel. Another notorious Nazi criminal was going on trial. This one had earned himself the horrific nickname of "Ivan the Terrible," but his given name was John Demjanjuk. It was just a name, John Demjanjuk.

When Gerhard saw Demjanjuk's picture, he remembered him. Demjanjuk had visited Gerhard's house as his father's guest when Gerhard was just a boy. The strangest thing was when Gerhard tried to jog his memory of the man. All he could remember was a kind, smiling face, a man who reminded him a great deal of his father.

There was nothing exceptional at all about Demjanjuk. He could be a man you might sit beside on the subway or pass on the street or in the market, and you would never know he had the black heart of a mass murderer. Gerhard could not comprehend how these ordinary men could have been able to commit such atrocities. What kind of evil possessed them? No matter how hard he tried, he could not understand their cruelty.

His mind ran constantly with a thousand unanswerable questions. Of course, he questioned. Every day of his life was a reminder of the shame that weighed on his shoulders because of his father. His father, the man who had spawned him—the man whose blood ran through his veins was one of them, but not just one of them, but a murderer of innocent human beings.

Papa, Gerhard had called him. Papa had smiled and lifted him high in the air when he returned home from work. They'd played ball outside and gone fishing together. It wasn't until later, after Papa was dead, that Gerhard learned the truth.

His gentle, adoring father was *SS Obersturmführer* Hans Helmut, who killed women and children in cold blood. Every morning, looking polished and handsome in his uniform, Gerhard's father kissed his mother gently, touched the baby's cheek, and ruffled Gerhard's hair tenderly before leaving for work.

How foolish Gerhard had been. After all, he was only a child. But the name of the place where his father was employed, Ravens-brück Concentration Camp, sounded to him like it was an outdoor retreat: a camp, like a summer camp, perhaps a place where people went to enjoy the country.

When Gerhard learned that his father had spent his days viciously killing people, mostly women, Gerhard denied that it could be true. His college professor had been the one to tell him what had really gone on at Ravensbrück, and his initial response towards his teacher was anger. He'd immediately dropped the class.

How do you turn your back on a man you loved and admired? A man who stayed up all night with you when you were running a fever or who proudly shook your hand when you excelled in your sports challenges in the *Hitler Jugend*, a man who taught you to respect women the way that he respected your mother? Who were you, Papa? Did I ever really know you?

The very idea that the man who'd raised him was a stranger gave Gerhard pangs of anxiety. It was true that when Gerhard was growing up, he had heard all about the Jews and all about the wickedness that they brought to the world; all about how dangerous they were. In fact, he'd been told that they were known to kidnap Christian children, drain their blood, and drink it. There had been speeches given to the boys in the *Jugend*, and then the same warning had been reinforced every day in school. His parents, too, had told him to beware of Jews, but there was no need for them to worry.

He'd never had any opportunity to socialize with anyone who was Jewish, so he'd never given it much thought. Gerhard had been a happy, carefree child who was kept far away from any Jewish influence. He'd been privileged to have grown up in blissful ignorance of the horrors of the Third Reich. Perhaps that was why learning the truth of what had been taking place had been such a shock. Murders, the murders of women and children committed by his father, were beyond his comprehension. But his own father? It was unfathomable.

How carefully those facts had been hidden from the innocent boy Gerhard had been. He was just a child who enjoyed the outdoor sports, the camaraderie of the Jugend, and the advantage of having grown up with a sense of entitlement to all the benefits of having a father with an important job in the Nazi party.

But, once he discovered the truth about the Jews and the Nazis, the hideous knowledge could not be forced back into the Pandora's Box whence it came. No, instead, it gnawed at his brain and his heart with the sharp teeth of a rat until, finally, he traveled to see the concentration camp where his father had worked.

He had hoped that, somehow, he would find what he'd been told was a lie, but it was there at Ravensbrück that he learned that what he feared had happened during the war was true. As a child, he'd never been allowed to visit the camp. His mother said his father was too busy and too important at his job to keep an eye on a child.

So, Gerhard had not entered Ravensbrück before. His first walk through the gates of Ravensbrück had taken place well after the liberation. He was led on a tour of what seemed like a horror movie.

The tour guide told Gerhard and the group that the gas chamber was destroyed a week before the camp was liberated. However, he explained how it was all done.

People were forced into the shower room. They were told they were being given a shower that would delouse them. The shower room was filled to capacity. The people were naked and smashed together, unable to move: women, children, old men, infants. Then, as they were waiting for the water from the shower to come down over them, pellets of Zyklon-B were dropped into the chamber. The gas was poisonous, and its effect on humans was hideous, resulting in painful death.

From a small window at the side of the gas chamber, the Nazi officers watched as the victims of the gas climbed over each other, pulverizing the infants in an effort to breathe.

Gerhard was appalled as he took a moment to look through the window and visualize the genocide that had taken place in this very room. Had his father stood in this very place and watched without doing anything to stop the killings? He felt the vomit rise in his throat. Even though he was with a group of people and had tried to run out before he embarrassed himself, it was too late. The vomit spewed from his lips, and he stood shocked, paralyzed and horrified.

One of the other visitors also happened to be a child of a member of the Nazi party. In a quiet, reassuring voice, she whispered to Gerhard that she did not believe the gas chamber had ever existed. He could not answer her. His body was trembling, and a sick feeling in Gerhard's heart assured him that all the accusations against the Nazi party were true.

Along the walls of Ravensbrück, Gerhard saw pictures of dead skeletal bodies piled like garbage, their bones jutting out of their chests. There were more photos. These were of emaciated prisoners —their dark eyes stared at him. He could almost hear their cries of pain, their voices in unison asking, 'Why?'

All the evidence he saw that day in Ravensbrück became imprinted like a bloodstain in his mind. How many deaths had his dear papa been responsible for? How many women, mothers, sisters, and daughters had perished by his father's hand, that same hand that had ruffled his hair and written out arithmetic problems to help him learn to add and subtract.

Gerhard wanted to forgive his father. In fact, he could still see Papa's well-manicured nails as he held the sharpened pencil and smiled up at Gerhard. "All right, son, let's see how fast you can solve these problems." Then he'd handed Gerhard the pencil.

Papa. Gerhard wanted to cry out, "Papa, why? Why, Papa? How could you do it?" They were simple math problems, but for a five-year-old child, they were challenging. However, Papa never made them so difficult that Gerhard could not solve them. He was a father who had helped his son to build confidence.

How could a man so kind and loving to his family be so cruel to others? Gerhard could find no peace in his soul. To deny his love for his father felt like a betrayal, but how could he love a man who was, in truth, a monster?

He'd tried to talk to his mother, but she denied that his father had any involvement in the killings. In fact, she denied that the killings took place at all. She told Gerhard that the only people whom the Nazis punished were political prisoners, enemies of the state. Gerhard knew better. The voice of his soul roared at him so loudly that he could not ignore the ranting.

Finally, he'd decided that the only way he could live with his shame was to have a doctor sterilize him so he would never have a child. Thereby, he could stop the bloodline of his father. Perhaps then his mind would be at rest. His younger brother, Max, thought Gerhard was crazy to act so irrationally. But it was something Gerhard felt strongly about, and he had it done.

The act of sterilization certainly contributed to his divorce. His wife felt that he should have consulted her before acting so irrationally. She was angry, very angry. Their communication broke down. Although they lived in the same house, they did not speak or make love. That was when she began to take lovers, and the marriage deteriorated. He understood how she felt but did what he felt he must do to make amends for his father's sins.

Still, it was not enough. He couldn't find serenity. And so, Gerhard began to study the Holocaust with vigor. He felt he must learn as much as he possibly could. Perhaps then he would find some peace. Somewhere in all the information Gerhard gathered must be the answers to all the questions robbing him of his peace of mind and invading his sleep.

Then, when Demjanjuk was extradited, Gerhard followed the old SS officer to Israel. Gerhard remembered Demjanjuk. He'd come to visit his father once. Gerhard would try to request an audience with Demjanjuk. Perhaps, if Gerhard could look directly into Demjanjuk's eyes and talk to him, ask Demjanjuk to reveal the truth about Gerhard's father, then Gerhard might finally rest. Somehow, he might understand how ordinary men, especially his beloved papa, could be capable of these terrible things.

After taking a long, hot shower, Gerhard dressed and took the elevator down to the main floor of the hotel. It had been a long day, and he had somehow forgotten to eat.

The restaurant in the hotel looked busy, but he was far too tired to wander the streets, so he gave the host his name and sat down on the sofa in the lobby to wait until his table was available. He'd been told that it would be a half hour before he got a table, so Gerhard picked up a magazine and began to read. It was good that he'd studied English in college because everything was written in Hebrew and English, and he didn't know any Hebrew.

A pretty girl with long auburn hair sat down beside him. She seemed anxious. Gerhard smiled at her.

"Good evening," he said.

"Hi."

He could tell by her accent that she was American. "I'm Gerhard."

"I'm Bari Lynn."

"It's a pleasure to meet you."

She smiled. He was handsome. His features were carved like a statue of a Greek god. His hair was the color of antique brushed gold, and his eyes matched his hair perfectly, a deep dark yellow, like a midnight sun. Bari looked down at the coffee table. It was hard to meet his eyes. She felt self-conscious. She felt ugly and unattractive after what happened earlier that day with Ido. "Are you visiting Israel?" she asked, not knowing what else to say to keep the conversation going.

"Yes, you could say that. And you? Are you visiting? I think I detect an American accent?"

"You're right. I'm from the States. I'm here with a group on tour."

He nodded. "So, how do you like it here so far?"

"I don't know." She shrugged, thinking about Ido and how much she wished she'd never come to Israel.

"I'm alone. Would you like to join me for dinner?"

"Oh, I don't know. I'm waiting for my girlfriend. Can she come, too?"

"Of course. Two American girls, what a treat for me." He smiled again. He was lonesome, and having company for dinner would take his mind off his problems at least for an hour or two. "I put my name on the list in the restaurant for a table. It might be a while."

He was older, a little balding, but still damned handsome, Bari thought.

Just then, Marilyn walked off the elevator and over to Bari Lynn.

"This is my friend, Marilyn." Bari introduced Gerhard to Marilyn.

"My pleasure," Gerhard said, extending his hand. Marilyn shook his hand. Bari could see her blush. "I was just asking your friend here if the two of you girls would like to join me for dinner."

Marilyn smiled, shrugged, and said, "Sure, why not?"

CHAPTER TWENTY-FOUR

THE FOLLOWING DAY, Elan returned from work early. He'd promised Noa that he would take her into the city to buy new ballet slippers. She had been complaining that hers were getting too small. They would shop for slippers and then have dinner before returning home.

Elan poured a shot of whiskey as he waited for Noa to finish dressing. Then he leaned against the countertop in the kitchen and noticed that the light on his answering machine was blinking. It was rare that anyone left him a message unless it was work, and he'd just left the office, so he was pretty sure that it was not them calling. Perhaps it was Katja, he thought, and his heart skipped a beat. Elan Amsel pressed the message button on the machine and listened.

"Mr. Amsel. My name is Ido Hadar. I am in charge of a group of Jewish–American teenagers who are touring Israel with their synagogue. I don't know how to tell you this, sir, but I have failed you terribly. Your daughter, Bari Lynn Allen, has gone missing. I am hoping that she is with you.

"She told me that she was here in Israel looking for you. So, I am assuming that she might have made contact with you already. Please telephone me and let me know if you have seen her. We are very concerned about her safety. So please call as soon as you get this. My number is 546-7488. I will wait by the phone for your call."

Beep, Beep, Beep. The machine made this noise to indicate that the caller had hung up.

Elan was puzzled. He tilted his head to a side, and his eyes scrunched as he thought about the call. He didn't know of anyone named Bari Lynn Allen. His only child was Noa, and she was in the other room getting dressed. In fact, from where he stood, Elan could hear Noa singing to herself as she was getting ready.

There must be some mistake. But still, someone's daughter had gone missing. What was this all about? It sounded like a young person was in trouble in Israel. If there was a child who needed help, especially a Jewish child in Israel, Elan would certainly do what he could. That was his way; it had always been his way. He replayed the message so that he could write down the phone number, and then he picked up the receiver. Elan would return this Ido fellow's call and find out what the hell was happening.

The phone only rang once.

"This is Ido Hadar…"

"This is Elan Amsel."

"I'm so glad you called back. I don't even know where to start, but I will try. I met your daughter a couple of days ago. She came to Israel with her synagogue. Her name is Bari Lynn Allen. Before she went missing, she told me that she was going to look for you while she was here. Apparently, her mother had not told her that you were her father until a few months ago. Once she found out that she had a father who was alive in Israel, she wanted to know more about you."

"This is clearly a mistake. It must be another man. I don't have a daughter by that name. But I am with Mossad, and I will go to the agency and see what we can do to help."

"Mr. Amsel. Do you know a woman by the name of Janice Lichtenstein? She's Bari Lynn's mother."

The shock of hearing the familiar name left Elan speechless. Janice was his ex-wife. It seemed like a thousand years ago, she'd left him and gone back to America. When she left him, she was pregnant. But she'd sent him a letter a few weeks later, telling him that she miscarried. He had no reason to doubt her. And at the time, he'd been relieved to be rid of her.

The marriage was not a good one. A sense of anguish spread over him. Could Bari Lynn be the child Janice was carrying when she returned home to America? Was she possibly lying to him when she said she had lost the baby? Elan felt a teardrop of sweat trickle down his chest.

"Mr. Amsel, are you still there?" Ido asked in a firm voice.

"Yes…" Elan cleared his throat. "Yes, I'm sorry. I'm just a little surprised to learn all of this. I know Janice Lichtenstein. She was my ex-wife, but I never knew we had a child. Can you get me her telephone number in America? I need to speak to her…"

"Of course, Mr. Amsel. Hold the line, and I'll get it for you…"

Elan's hand trembled as he held the receiver, waiting for the phone number that would send him on a freight train back into his past.

CHAPTER TWENTY-FIVE

GERHARD HAD AWAKENED EARLY that same morning. He called room service and ordered breakfast. When he'd talked to Max about coming to Israel, they'd both been drinking, and it sounded like a perfect plan. But now that he was here, he was finding it hard to go to the prison where Demjanjuk was being held and ask to see him. The night he'd decided to make the trip, in his drunken stupor, it had seemed logical to him to go to the prison and claim to be a journalist. Now, that seemed foolish.

The madness that had been haunting him was subsiding, and he began to feel intimidated. If he told the Israeli officials the truth, the real reason he'd come, what would they think of him? After all, was he not his father's son?

Gerard ran his fingers through his hair, shaking his head as he realized how irrational he'd been to come here. It had cost him all of his savings. He was a civil engineer, and he made a decent living, but his ex-wife had an addiction to redecorating the house, so there wasn't much left after the divorce. What was he thinking, spending everything he had to come to a country that would undoubtedly condemn him for his father's sins?

There was a knock at the door of his hotel room. It must be the food he'd ordered from room service. Gerhard took a few shekels out of his pants pocket to tip the delivery person and opened the door.

CHAPTER TWENTY-SIX

"Janice?" Elan had dreaded making this call. It had been eighteen years since he'd heard her voice.

"Elan…" Janice and Lucas were sitting on the sofa, waiting for a second call from the Israeli police.

"Yes, it's me," he said.

"Oh my God, Elan." Janice was hysterical. "I got a call from the Israeli police. Bari Lynn has gone missing. If something has happened to her, I will never forgive myself for having allowed her to go to Israel."

"You never told me anything about Bari Lynn…"

"She's your daughter, Elan, and I am praying that she is all right. Help me, please. Tell me the truth, Elan. You must tell me, is she with you?"

There was an uncomfortable silence. Lucas sat beside Janice and remained silent. She was furious with him. After all, he was the reason she'd finally agreed to allow Bari to go to Israel, and now…

"I am still in a state of shock. First, I didn't even know I had a child, and then I found out she had gone missing."

"So, Bari is not with you?"

"No, she is not with me."

"She should be showing up there anytime. I am sure she's gone looking for you. You're not keeping the truth from me, are you? I mean, as a punishment for not telling you that you had a daughter? Is she with you? Please, Elan, please tell me she is."

"I wish I could. If she were here, I would tell you, Janice. I am not vengeful. In fact, I'm worried. If she is missing, she could be in trouble."

"Yes, I know. But I am hoping that she will show up at your door very soon or call you."

"I hope so. Then, at least, we will know she is safe. But until she arrives, I am going to have to act as if she is in danger. In situations like this, time is of the essence. I will go into the office at Mossad and begin the proceedings to find a missing person."

"Mossad? The secret police?"

"I work there, Janice. I am a Mossad agent."

"Oh… I didn't know."

"Of course, you didn't. We haven't spoken for eighteen years. A lot has happened."

"I'm coming to Israel. I have to find my daughter. When I get there, how can I find you?"

"I'll give you my number; call me when you arrive. But listen to me, Janice, this is very important. Make sure that you don't tell anyone about Bari Lynn being missing. It is best to keep this situation quiet until we know what is happening. If the word leaks out too early, it could cost us Bari's life. It all depends on where she is, if she's out looking for me, or if she's been kidnapped. And if she's been kidnapped, who has taken her and why? At this point, we just don't know. So don't talk to anyone, not the police, not anyone. Do you understand?"

"Yes…" Janice felt her hand trembling and sweating as she held the receiver.

After Janice had hung up the phone, she turned to Lucas. He sat beside her quietly. There were tears in her eyes. She'd never considered that Bari could be in real danger. In fact, when she was told that Bari had strayed from the group, she'd been certain that Bari was with Elan.

"I'm going to Israel to get my daughter…"

"I'm coming with you."

"You realize that this is all your fault? All we had to do was say no when she asked us to go."

"Yes, I know all about it. I'm sorry. You know I love Bari as much as you do, and I am sick with worry," Lucas said.

"I know you love her, but this was a mistake. You couldn't possibly love her as much as I do. After all, you're not her real father," Janice said, but she was immediately sorry when she saw the hurt on Lucas's face. Damn, she always spoke without thinking. "I'm sorry. That was wrong of me. You've been a good father to her. I know you would never have agreed to allow her to go to Israel if you thought she was in danger. I'm just scared."

"It's all right. We don't need to fight. Right now, we need to give each other strength. Come on, let's pack. Let's go and find our daughter," Lucas said, gently rubbing her shoulder.

She looked up at him. "I told you it was a bad idea for her to go to Israel. I knew. I knew, Lucas. Israel was really bad luck for me when I was younger. I tried to tell you that." Janice crossed her arms over her chest and glared at him.

CHAPTER TWENTY-SEVEN

THE SUN WAS so bright against the crystal-blue sky that it burst into Gerhard's hotel room through the window. Outside, the leaves on the treetops sparkled with the morning dew. It had been a day such as this when his father had passed away, the kind of day that was so beautiful it seemed as if nothing could go wrong. Except that for the Helmut family, everything had been shaken to its very core that day.

Gerhard was pulled back to that summer morning. He'd sat beside his mother and brother in the hospital room, watching, helpless as his father took his last breath. The doctors explained that he had no brain function. The only life left within him came from the machines filling his body with fluid and oxygen. It was made clear to the family that the machines must be turned off, and Gerhard's father must be allowed to go in peace.

His heart pounded as the two doctors and the nurse began shutting down his father's connection to life. Gerhard wanted to scream to say, "*No, you can't do this! He's not dead! Maybe he will come back.*" But it had been made very clear to the family that the man who lay on the table was already brain-dead.

His mother held Gerhard's arm so tightly that he felt her nails penetrating his flesh. She was terrified of losing her husband, her security, the only man she'd ever known.

Gerhard knew how hard it was for her. His parents were childhood sweethearts. They'd grown up living across the hall from each other in the same building. Then, when his mother was seventeen and his father was twenty, they married.

His father had been the oak tree that held the family together. Until his father began to work for the Nazis, the family was very poor. The Nazi party had given the Helmuts food, status, and a way of life that his parents had never dared to dream was possible.

Gerhard didn't remember the poverty and was too young to realize much. But he did remember the house outside of Ravensbrück, the garden, the friends he played ball with, and the boys whose fathers also worked at the camp. None of them ever discussed their father's work. It was just something taken for granted. He wondered if any of them knew what was really going on at the camp. He doubted it. They were too young to understand.

Then he remembered how tense things became in his house. At night, he would hear his parents whispering that Germany was losing the war. Gerhard had no idea what the consequences of this might be, but hearing the worry in his parents' voices made him afraid.

Then it happened: the war ended. The Americans, the British, and the Russians came barging into Germany. His mother held his shoulder as he watched the troops march in, wearing the uniforms that Helmut had been taught to fear. The invaders were cruel to the Germans, and Gerhard, who had been just a boy at the time, was frightened of them. They called the Germans murderers and devils.

At the time, Gerhard thought it was because of the war and all the soldiers that had been lost on the other side. Knowing that the victorious army had suffered many casualties worried Gerhard. Would they take their anger out on the German citizens, and if so, what would they do?

At first, his father had tried to make light of the situation, telling Gerhard that there was nothing to be afraid of and that this was how things were at the end of a war. Once again, Gerhard had wanted to believe. But then, things became more tense in the Helmut home. His parents were awake late into the night, speaking softly, words Gerhard could not hear or understand.

Then, one day, Gerhard returned from school to find that his father was gone. His mother explained that his father had to leave Germany. She made it clear to Gerhard and Max that the family did not know where he had gone. All they knew was that his father had been forced to go underground to hide because he was an important person in the Nazi party. It was several years before Gerhard heard from his papa.

His mother was poor, and money was scarce, but that was no surprise. All the Germans were poor. There were displaced Jews wandering the streets. They looked skeletal, their dark, sunken eyes fixed upon Gerhard, sending shivers through his body. Food was scarce. Gerhard and his brother were always hungry. He still remembered his mother going without eating, saying she was not hungry so her boys would have her share. God bless his poor mother.

But as hard as he tried, Gerhard could not forget the whispers of his neighbors and his parents' friends. There were things implied, things he didn't understand, things that were silenced when the children appeared.

These conversations were small indications of what had happened in the concentration camps. Of course, he had not been privy to the whole story. But if he were truly honest with himself, Gerhard would have to admit that he knew something—suspected something was terribly wrong with the work his father did at the camp. Deep down in his heart, hadn't he suspected that something had occurred at the camps, something terrible—but what and why?

Until the truth was forced upon him like a slap in his face, he refused to believe. When he could no longer deny his father's guilt, the truth was like an army tank running right over him and smashing his world into the ground.

A knock at the door forced Gerhard to come back to the moment. He assumed it must be room service. He took several bills out of his pocket to tip the delivery man. Gerhard felt like his mind was running away with him. He had come here to Israel for a reason.

There was another knock at the door.

"I'll be right there," Gerhard said, his robe closed before he opened the door. Again, his mind raced. How was he going to request a meeting with the imprisoned Nazi?

Gerhard opened the door.

"Are you Gerhard Helmut?"

It was an IDF soldier in uniform. Gerhard had no idea why the IDF would be at his door. He felt his heart begin to race. What did they want with him? They knew his name. Did they think he had something to do with his father? Or maybe they thought he'd come to help the Nazi escape. How would he ever make them understand why he'd come to Israel?

"Yes. I'm Gerhard Helmut," Gerhard said. The sound of his own name sounded like a curse word in his ear. It was the name he carried along with the sins of his father. He bit his lower lip.

"You're under arrest."

"What? Arrest? Why?" Could they arrest him for his father's crimes? Was that possible? Would he ever be able to make them believe that he was only a child when it all happened? Would they believe him when he told them that he'd felt guilty his entire life for what his father had done? He should never have come to Israel. This was the Jewish homeland. In the eyes of the Jews, Gerhard Helmut was the enemy.

Gerhard coughed a little as the soldier burst into his hotel room through the door. He could see the man from room service with his tray, standing dumbfounded behind the soldier outside the hallway.

"You were talking to two young girls last night in the lobby?" the soldier asked.

"Yes, I was." Gerhard cleared his throat. What would last night have to do with anything? What had he been accused of now? He was forty-eight, and his looks were beginning to fade. That was why he loved the attention of young women. But he hadn't tried to take the girls to his bed. He'd only taken the young girls to dinner. It made him feel good to walk into the restaurant in the company of pretty young women. He felt as if he were still desirable. This insecurity stemmed from his wife, Abigail, leaving him for another man less than a year before.

She'd never been satisfied with what he could provide for her, and after he had himself sterilized, she had had enough. She began staying out late and refusing to communicate with him. Then, when she met Norbert, who had an important position in international banking, she'd asked for a divorce. He knew that a good part of what had caused her loss of love for him stemmed from his obsession with his father's past.

Abigail hated the Nazis. She was ashamed of being German because of what had happened under Hitler. She had tried to coax Gerhard to leave the past behind, to pretend it had never happened. But her family had only been working people. They had not had a hand in the murders. She was able to forget. But Gerhard's father was directly involved, and he was haunted.

"What happened last night?" the soldier asked, stern and demanding.

"I'm sorry. I don't know what you mean."

"With the girls."

"Oh, nothing happened."

"Nothing?"

"I bought them dinner, we ate. I flirted, but then I went back to my room."

"What is an old man like you doing with two teenagers?"

"Nothing. I just like to flirt. But I would never do anything inappropriate."

"I see. You just like to flirt? To spend your money taking two girls to dinner, and then you expect nothing in return. Is that right?"

"Yes. That's all that happened."

"The girls have gone missing. They never returned to their hotel room last night. I have to take you to headquarters for questioning."

"Missing? What do you mean?"

"Get dressed, Mr. Helmut. You have five minutes."

Two hours later, when Elan arrived at the police station, it was filled with people. The stale odor of nervous energy and cigarette smoke lingered in the air.

Everyone from the tour group Bari had come to Israel with was now being questioned. There were teenagers and adults lined up in seats around the printer of the room. Some of the women were crying.

Elan had expected as much. His feelings were strange to him. On one hand, he felt terrible for the missing girl and Janice, but he really didn't know the child. Although she was his own blood, he had only just learned the news, and his heart was not grieving. Elan was angrier with Janice than he was upset about the kidnapping. How could she have lied to him for so long? If this tragedy had not occurred, he would never have known he had a daughter in America. That was Janice, a selfish, spoiled, rich girl.

Well, it wasn't Bari's fault, and he would do everything he could to find her. But he could not feel the same toward her as he did toward Noa. He'd raised Noa, held her as a baby when she cried, bathed her in rubbing alcohol to bring down her fever, and then walked the floors through the night with her when she was sick. Elan had been the one to take Noa to school on her first day. He'd helped her pick out a dress and all her supplies. These were events that would always be branded in his heart.

If Noa were missing, he would be out of his mind right now with worry and fear. In fact, he would undoubtedly be so shaken that he might be of no use to the police.

As angry as he was with Janice, he couldn't help but feel sorry for her. In one of the private rooms, he saw a middle-aged, fairly attractive man being questioned by a female police officer whom he believed he recognized. If he remembered correctly, her name was Tova Ben-Levi, but he couldn't be sure if it was her.

The night he'd met Tova, he'd been drunk. It was a long time ago when they were both much younger. It was before he'd met Nina. They spent a few hours together. He couldn't even remember if they'd been intimate. They probably had, and like most women from his past, she probably hated and resented him.

Yes, Elan had the reputation of being a cad. But that was before he'd married his dearest Nina. Now, he had no desire to spend intoxicated nights with random women. Instead, he stayed at home and watched his daughter, Noa—his beautiful, precious daughter who was growing up to look like her mother more every day.

"You must be Elan Amsel?" A young, very attractive Israeli man walked over and extended his hand. Elan assumed that it was Ido.

"Yes."

"I'm Ido."

"I thought as much." Elan smiled and shook Ido's hand. He studied Ido and was surprised at how much Ido reminded him of himself when he was younger.

"Come, I'm working out of a makeshift office here at the police station. It's not the best, but at least we'll have some privacy, and I can tell you what we have learned so far…"

Elan followed Ido into a small room with a desk and three chairs. Both men sat. The door opened, and a girl entered. Elan felt his heart stop. She was the spitting image of his first love, his first fiancé. How could anyone look so much like Katja did when she and Elan had first met?

The girl's blond hair fell into the same golden curls that Elan had never been able to forget. She had the same bright blue eyes. Elan looked at her and felt a deep emptiness, the loss of his youth, and a sting of regret for all the mistakes he'd made. He had made terrible mistakes with Katja. He'd hurt her badly, and he was so sorry that he had.

But if he had married Katja, then he would never have met Nina. So perhaps everything worked out the way it was supposed to work out. But still, he wished that he had been kinder, more understanding.

As Elan was aging, his heart was becoming softer. He assumed that was because of Noa. He would never want any man to treat Noa the way that he had treated women in his youth.

"Ido, we are detaining the German until we have further information. Tova is working on him, trying to find out everything she can," the lovely blonde who looked like Katja said.

"Thank you, Ima. I'll speak with Tova in a few minutes." Ima left the room.

So, it was Tova, Elan thought. At least his mind was not going. Elan sighed. Then he looked at the blonde again. Hadn't Katja mentioned that her daughter's name was Ima? Could that possibly be her daughter? He had to ask.

"That girl, the blonde who was just here, what's her last name?"

"Hadar. She's my wife," Ido said, bristling a little at the question. He wanted to be sure that Elan knew that Ima was his wife and not available for Elan's romantic pursuit.

"Oh, she just looks so much like someone I've known for a long time. Was her maiden name Zaltstein?"

"Yes, in fact, it was."

"I know her mother," Elan said. What a small world. He wondered if Ido knew about Katja's real parents. If he did, that would mean he was a bigger and smarter man than Elan. He'd married the woman he loved in spite of her bloodlines. But if he didn't, was it Elan's responsibility to tell him? Did Ido have a right to know? If Elan did tell him, what would be the consequences? No, Elan would not tell him. Why? There was no point. It was best to mind his own business.

For now, Elan would try to keep his mind on the case. He had a daughter, who was somewhere in Israel, a child of his blood. Elan was having enough trouble trying to process all the new information about his newly discovered daughter, who was now in danger.

"All right, Ido. Show me everything you have about the case so far. Also, I want all the information that you got from each of the other tourists from the synagogue. I need to know what the German said when he was questioned. Then, I will take everything and go to Mossad. We will review it and go from there. Can you have everything for me by this afternoon?"

"Yes, sir. Would you like it sent to your office?"

"Yes, as soon as you can."

"Okay, Mr. Amsel. I will have all of that compiled and brought to you, and I will stay in touch and make sure that you are informed of everything as new information is gathered."

Elan nodded, got up, and walked out of Ido's office. As he turned to leave the police station, he glanced at Tova. She was intent on her conversation with the German. Elan studied her for a moment.

Tova was plain, not ugly, not beautiful, but she had an honest face. Her body was heavyset and a little flabby, but she wasn't really fat. He remembered now. He had slept with her once long ago. Looking at her, he wondered why he'd even done that. Had she been more attractive then? Or was he just drunk and careless, as he had been so much of the time in his youth?

In fact, now he wondered how he could have gone through a string of sexual partners without any feelings, names, and faces he couldn't even remember. He had hurt a lot of people when he was a young man. Then Nina awakened something in Elan that would never allow him to be callous about love again. Poor Tova. Elan hoped that she'd gone on to find happiness in her life.

Tova Ben-Levi had interrogated many criminals in the past fifteen years she'd worked for the Israeli police. She was known amongst her coworkers to be tough and relentless. Most of all, she was blessed with a keen instinct that enabled her to spot a liar, and she was almost never wrong.

She'd been handpicked for this investigation because she spoke perfect English and was fluent in German. This suspect was of German descent. She would try to talk to him in English; if that didn't work, she could easily switch to German. Now, sitting across from Gerhard Helmut, the more she questioned him, the more she was convinced that he was not involved in any kidnapping or illegal activity with the missing girls.

He'd taken them to dinner. Why? He admitted it made him feel young and desirable to be seen with two girls half his age. Disgusting, perhaps, criminal, no. Gerhard had told her that after dinner, he went back to his room alone. Tova had been browbeating Gerhard for four hours, asking the same questions repeatedly, rewording them, and trying to get a different answer. His story remained the same, and Tova believed him by what she could see in his eyes.

"So, you came here to Israel to take young girls to dinner?" she asked, tapping her pencil on the desk and biting her lower lip as she watched his reaction to her questions. Tova was thorough and knew from experience that the answers were less important than the facial and body expressions of the person she was questioning. She was determined to find out anything and everything about Gerhard Helmut before she would allow him to leave the police station.

"No, of course not. I just happened to meet the girls in the lobby. I was going to eat alone. But when they started to talk to me, I figured, well, at least, I would have some company."

"Hmm," Tova said. "And you wanted nothing from these girls in exchange for the thirty dollars you spent on them for dinner?"

"I knew they were too young for anything like that." He blushed. Gerhard came from a conservative background. Things like this were never discussed aloud. "But I am a lonely man," Gerhard said. "I just wanted to talk to someone to take my mind off things," and he wasn't lying. When he met the girls, he just wanted to relieve the constant chatter in his brain by talking with other people for a few hours rather than going over his thoughts like a broken record.

"What kind of things were you trying to take your mind off?" she asked.

He shrugged. "Just things."

"You are a visitor here in Israel?" She got up and walked behind him. Tova knew that having a police officer standing behind a suspect always put the suspect on edge. When a person was nervous, they sometimes blurted out things they were trying to hide.

"Yes," Gerhard said. He was uneasy being questioned like a criminal. He had done nothing to those girls. In fact, now that he learned that they were missing, he was worried about them.

They were two nice American kids. For an hour or so, they'd humored him. They laughed at his jokes and listened to his amusing stories. It had made him feel young and still attractive. But it was best not to talk too much about this to the police. Although his intentions were honorable, he felt his behavior might make him seem a little perverted. Gerhard was afraid that he was about to be terribly misunderstood.

"Your passport says that you are here from Germany. It seems strange to me that you arrived on the same day as Demjanjuk. Do you know who that is?" Tova had done some research before going in to interrogate Helmut.

Gerhard took a deep breath and ran his hand through his thinning, blond hair. "Yes. I know who he is."

"And perhaps you have come here because of him?"

"Yes. I've come because of him." Why lie? He might as well just come clean with the truth. This was his opportunity to ask for an audience with Demjanjuk. He hoped his madness wouldn't end in his incarceration for some crime he had not committed. But he had come so far, and this need to understand his father had haunted him for too long.

"Oh? You are a Nazi supporter, then?" Tova returned to her seat behind her desk but remained standing and stared into Gerhard's eyes.

"No—not a supporter," Gerhard said, shaking his head, his shoulders slumped. Then, in a soft, cracking voice, he said, "I am the son of an SS officer. I've come here to try to find out what made my father do what he did. I've been carrying his guilt since I learned what happened. My father is dead. So, I cannot ask him why…" Gerhard coughed and cleared his throat… "or how he could do what he did."

"So, you came here to do exactly what?" Tova leaned forward so that her face was close to Gerhard's.

"I was going to see if I might be able to go to the prison and ask to see Demjanjuk. I remember meeting him once as a boy. I was just a child when he came to my house as a friend of my father's. But you see, I had no idea what was happening in the camps. To me and to my family, my father was a kind and loving man. I have to know first if it is true that my father did these things, and then I have to know why. For me to make peace with life, I must have answers."

Gerhard's skin had turned the color of ripe radishes. His body was trembling, and his hands gripped the chair's arms.

"You don't believe that the Holocaust happened? You don't believe that innocent people were killed?" Tova had heard this bull-shit before. She wasn't going to let him get away with perpetuating this lie, not when so many of her friend's parents had been murdered by Hitler and his henchmen.

"I didn't want to believe anything so horrible could be real. I wanted to deny it. God knows I wanted to deny it. So many of my friends and family deny it. That is the only way that they can go on living without the constant guilt.

"But as hard as I tried, I couldn't. In fact, I've been so obsessed with shame that I went to the camps and saw everything... with my own eyes. I am heartsick. I know, deep in my gut, that it is true that my father did these things. But I came here in hopes that somehow, someway, perhaps this man Demjanjuk can make things clear to me so that I can pick up the pieces of my broken life..." Gerhard was speaking loudly, his voice cracking with emotion.

"An apology from me to your people is hardly enough. I've even had myself sterilized so that I can never spread the seed of my father. And yet, I still love him. That's part of the guilt, I guess. You see, no matter what he was, he was my father..." Gerhard was weeping now.

Tova had never seen a man weep like this. She was not a soft woman, not at all. She'd been in the IDF, worked at the police department, and seen hardened criminals. And yet, this man had touched a soft place inside her with the sincerity of his pain.

"Okay, why don't we take a break for a while? I'll have someone bring you a glass of water," she said and left the room.

Outside the interrogation room, Ido approached Tova and pulled her over to the side of the building, away from the crowds of people.

"So, what do you think?" Ido asked.

"I say he's not guilty of anything. He took a couple of young girls to dinner. But I really believe that's all he did."

CHAPTER TWENTY-EIGHT

ELAN LEFT the police department and drove directly to his office at Mossad. When he arrived, he found people rushing in all directions. Elan had been with Mossad long enough to know by the electric atmosphere that something was happening. Elan grabbed the shirt-sleeve of one of his coworkers, stopping him in his tracks.

"What the hell is going on here?" Elan asked.

"A letter was dropped at the door less than five minutes ago. Those two American girls who were here with their synagogue were kidnapped by the FPN. We just got a letter from the FPN. They are demanding that we release ten of their top members, or they will kill the girls."

The FPN was a group of radical Palestinians whose specialty was bombings and kidnappings. The letters stood for Free Palestine Now. It was a small faction of radical and violent people determined to take back the land along the Gaza Strip. Israel was well aware of their tactics.

The group did not boast large numbers, but the Palestinian community often offered moral support, food, and even money when needed. However, not every Palestinian supported terrorism. Some people wanted to end the violence so they could live in peace.

"Who dropped off the letter?"

"Nobody knows. Nobody saw anything."

"One of those girls who was kidnapped is my daughter. Where is this letter?"

"Your daughter, Noa? No, it can't be Noa. These are American girls. They came here with a synagogue from the United States, from Chicago in Illinois."

"Yes, I know. Never mind. It's a long story. Which prisoners do the FPN want us to give them, and how long do we have?"

"I have a list. They're definitely FPN. The men they want to be released are radical terrorists. They've committed horrible crimes that resulted in the deaths of many innocent people. We can't just release them. They've given us seventy-two hours. It's hardly enough time, but if we agree to their demands and exchange prisoners for hostages, it will open up an avenue where terrorists will think all they have to do is capture some prisoners, and Israel will bend to their will."

"I know all of this. You're wasting my time. Where in the hell is the letter?" Elan growled.

"Come on, let me show you. You can read it for yourself."

CHAPTER TWENTY-NINE

BARI LYNN AWAKENED with a ferocious headache. Her hands and feet were bound, and she was blindfolded. Bari Lynn felt a shock of panic grip her stomach. The restriction of her bonds heightened her fears. She suddenly felt as if she couldn't breathe. *Slow down, Bari. Try to remember what Dad taught you about meditating. Stay calm.* God, she wished Lucas was here with her.

She'd studied martial arts with him for all those years, and now, when she needed to fight, she was weak and terrified. Then Bari remembered Marilyn. *Was she here, too?*

"Mar, are you here?" she called out in the darkness.

"I'm here," she whimpered. "My head feels like I've been hit by a truck, and I gotta pee!"

"Same here. You otherwise all right?"

"Nothing that an extra-strength Excedrin, a hot shower, and a massage couldn't cure."

"Yeah. Me, too," Bari said. *Thank God. At least she is still alive and unhurt.*

What had happened? Where was she? It was dank and filthy, and it seemed as if she must be somewhere underground. A moist, musty odor penetrated her nostrils. The floor on which she sat was not a floor at all but dirt and rocks. *Think, Bari, try to remember what happened the previous night and how did I end up here?*

She and Marilyn had dinner with that older guy, the one with the German accent. He seemed nice. He'd bought them drinks even though they were underage. Was he responsible for their situation now? But how? If she remembered correctly, he'd said goodnight to them.

Then they walked him to the elevator, and he went to his room. After that, she and Marilyn had gone off to a nightclub. Bari had not had a lot of exposure to alcohol, so she'd been affected more strongly than she realized.

Bari could remember that she and Marilyn had gone to several different clubs. They'd danced with lots of older guys. At the time, she'd loved the numbing effect of drinking and the excitement of the music. It helped her forget how lousy she felt about the rejection from Ido earlier that afternoon.

"Move closer to me, and I will do the same," Bari said, wiggling her body closer to Marilyn.

"Okay."

It was hard to move. Bari's entire body ached, and it felt like she was bruised all over. In the darkness, she could hear Marilyn inching toward her, and Bari realized that her friend was crying.

She wanted to cry, too. But all she could do was wiggle her body slowly closer to Marilyn. It took a long time, but finally, Bari was close enough to lean against her friend. The comfort of the warmth of a familiar body helped ease some of the panic. The two girls were lying on the dirt floor side-by-side, crying softly, Bari wishing Lucas was there to help her.

Marilyn drifted in and out of sleep, but Bari could not rest. She was alert when the sounds of male voices came from somewhere above them. The voices spoke in Arabic, but she couldn't understand what they were saying. Their tone was angry. She knew there were several voices, and they were quite agitated.

Kazim Nasir loved his older brother, Fadi. They'd built this group of dedicated people who worked together to reclaim the land that was stolen from Palestine by Israel. Now, his brother Fadi was in prison, along with several other members of their FPN cell. Yes, they could be called violent, but how else does one deal with people like the Jews, who demand everything, and the American infidels who support them? Secretly, he couldn't help but admire the Israelis. They were relentless and fearless, and nothing stopped them. But he hated them too for everything they'd taken from him. Along with their American allies, they'd destroyed his family, killed his dear father, imprisoned his brother and best friend, and stolen his dignity and country.

And, of course, there was always that lesson from what had happened with the athletes in Munich. They'd learned the hard way that Israel didn't negotiate with terrorists. The Israelis would rather see the death of their people, rather than give in to the demands placed upon them. They had learned from Operation Wrath of God that the accursed Mossad would hunt them down in any country, even if it took twenty years.

They didn't forget, and they didn't forgive. If his group slipped up, it would be a certain death for them all. But they would not slip up. His cell has strict orders not to discuss the girls with anyone, and they would keep the hostages blindfolded.

However, America was another story. They wanted to appear humane in the eyes of the world. He had two Jewish-American girls in the cellar, and he was pretty sure that they were worth a fortune in Palestinian lives. If he threatened to kill them, America would intervene, and there was a damned good chance they would exchange his brother and the rest of their members for these two kaffirs, these detestable scum.

Elected American presidents could not stand the media heat of kidnappings. Wasn't it true that Ronald Reagan defeated Jimmy Carter in the election because of the hostages at the American Embassy in Iran? They were fools to show that they could yield to kidnapping.

True, President Reagan was more decisive in his stance against terrorism, but he did not always agree with Israel, either. Perhaps this would be the wedge they could drive between the Americans and the Israelis. Kazim smiled—soon, they could renew the fight to reclaim their land and force the filthy Jews out.

Now, his younger brother, Athir, was a different person altogether. He was always challenging Kazim to rethink his ideas, and as far as Kazim was concerned, that was dangerous.

Athir was his brother, and Kazim trusted him with his life, but Athir was not a firm believer in the methods of the FPN. He was constantly warning Kazim that following the FPN was sure to get them both killed. Kazim knew that Athir wanted to go to America to study medicine, and it tortured Kazim to know that his own brother was being swayed by the *kaffirs*.

Kazim considered the Holy Qur'an. 1:194—"If anyone transgresses against you, you also may retaliate against them to an equal extent. Have fear of God and know that He supports the pious." Kazim was not a religious man, nor were most of the other members of his group. Still, he used the scriptures wherever possible to keep the troops motivated.

The real reason for his hate was the loss of their land, and for that, he would use any means necessary—the scriptures, bombs, guns—whatever it took to fight the accursed Jews for the rest of his life.

Even worse than Athir was his mother. Kazim's mother was constantly begging him to stay out of trouble, to go to school, and try to live side-by-side with the kafirs. He knew it was because she had already suffered the death of her husband and lost one of her sons to a life of imprisonment. But she was a woman, and women had no place in making decisions. It grieved him that it made her heartsick to see her sons in trouble.

It had taken great convincing for Kazim to persuade Athir to be a part of this kidnapping. Athir had wanted nothing to do with all of this, but Kazim knew how badly Athir longed for his brother Fadi to be released from prison. Even so, Athir had not agreed until the members of the FPN had promised Athir that they would not hurt the girls. Even so, the greater FPN organization would kill them if they let the girls go free without the release of the prisoners. They would have to kill them if they didn't get what they wanted. The FPN would lose face and be unable to do successful kidnappings in the future.

The ransom letters had been delivered early that morning by a group of local children who were under ten years old. They were grooming these children as new recruits for the FPN. The FPN was reasonably confident that, because of their age, these kids could walk around without attracting much attention. A copy of the letter was sent to Mossad, one to the offices of the Prime Minister of Israel and another to the American Embassy.

"How long has it been since you've given the two girls any food or water?" Athir asked.

"We haven't given them anything. They've only been here for a short time," one of the members said.

"That's not right. I'll bring them something to eat and drink."

Athir took a bottle of water and a loaf of pita and climbed down into the cellar. The odor of damp earth greeted him. In one hand, he carried the food and water. In the other, he held a high-powered flashlight.

"I've brought you something to eat and drink," Athir said. He had studied English for several years in school, so he spoke it fairly well. He hoped his fluent English would help him as he tried to find a way to attend college in America.

"I have to go to the bathroom," Bari said.

A hole in the corner of the room had been dug for use as a makeshift bathroom.

Athir unbound Bari's feet and helped her up off the ground. Even blindfolded, she grabbed his wrist and tried to kick him, but she was dizzy and fell over. How could her martial arts training fail her now?

"Don't do that again," he said. "I'm warning you. Or I will leave you without food or water and to rot in your own filth."

She could hear the anger in his voice, and she was suddenly frightened.

Athir stood over Bari Lynn as she urinated. It was an embarrassing moment for him. He had not wanted to be involved in this mission at all, and now, here he was, acting like a terrorist. Once she finished, he bound her legs.

She was afraid to try to fight him again. It was obvious to her that she had been given drugs to ensure she would lose consciousness. That was how they must have taken her. Her drinks had probably been tampered with. Now, the drugs had left her weak and unfocused. If she tried to fight again and failed, he might hurt her or Marilyn.

Once her legs were bound, Athir took Marilyn to the makeshift latrine to pee. Once she returned, Marilyn sat beside Bari, and Athir bound her legs again.

"Listen to me," Athir said. "I know you want to try to fight and get away, but it is no use. Your captors are right upstairs, and they have guns. Never attempt to take the blindfolds off. The day that you see our faces, you will die. Do not scream. No one but my partners upstairs will hear you, and it will make them angry.

"I have been assigned to take care of you. I will not hurt you as long as you cooperate. The others are very angry with Americans and Jews, and some of them would like to kill you. They probably won't shoot you because they need you, but they could hurt you badly if you cause any trouble. Don't make me sorry that I tried to be kind to you."

Bari Lynn nodded.

"I have a gun," he said, his voice cracking with nervousness. "Please, just eat and drink. Don't cause any trouble. I don't want to hurt you."

"You speak good English," Marilyn said.

"Almost everyone in our group speaks, at least, some English."

Both girls ate the bread and drank the water. Bari had never been this hungry before. Her captor was young, perhaps twenty or twenty-two at the most, by the sound of his voice. There was something else in his voice. Was that a sense of regret that she detected?

He cleared his throat. "I'm sorry that we have to do this to you," he said. "I know you're scared…"

It was regret, Bari thought. She could hear the apology in his voice, and she felt a glimmer of hope.

"Why did they kidnap us?"

"You are hostages to be exchanged for the release of some of our members from prison."

"What happens if you don't get what you want?"

"May Allah be merciful," he said in a quivering voice.

Just then, a male voice came from upstairs like a roar of thunder.

"Athir, tie them back up and come up here. I need your help now!"

"Your name is Athir?" Bari Lynn asked boldly. She'd once heard that if someone was attacking you, it was best to find his or her human side: ask them their name, tell them yours, and ask about their families.

"Now, Athir!"

"I'm coming, Kazim."

"Yes. My name is Athir."

"I'm Bari Lynn. This is my best friend, Marilyn," she said.

"Athir…" His brother was calling him.

"I don't need to know your name." Athir looked away from her and stared at the door leading upstairs. A trickle of sweat tickled his brow and dripped into his eye. "I'm sorry," Athir said to Bari and Marilyn, and she heard the sound of the door closing and the falling of his footsteps as he climbed the stairs.

CHAPTER THIRTY

WHEN JANICE and Lucas arrived at the Ben Gurion Airport in Israel, they didn't even stop to drop their luggage off at the hotel. Instead, they took a taxi right to the offices of Mossad. Elan was at his desk and on the phone with the prime minister when his secretary informed him that he had visitors.

He glanced out his office door and saw Janice sitting on the old sofa in the waiting room. She'd aged. Her once flaming-red mane was now short and styled. Her slender shape had filled out, but her face was red, and deep lines had formed between her eyes from the after-effects of weeping.

A man with long hair sat beside her, holding her hand. *That must be her husband. That must be the man who raised my child.* Elan had a strange feeling in the pit of his stomach.

Just seeing Janice again transported Elan back to the time when she was his wife. It was hard to believe that once, so long ago, they'd been married and divorced. But it was even harder for Elan to comprehend that she had borne him a child, a girl he'd never known about until only a few days ago.

A part of him was angry with Janice for all the years she'd lied to him. He wanted to give her a piece of his mind, to tell her just what he thought of her deceitful behavior. But seeing Janice sitting beside her husband with her head on his shoulder and so much pain in her eyes, Elan couldn't help but feel sorry for her. She'd stolen his child from him, but she was a mother that was terrified and desperate. How would he feel if Noa was missing?

"Yes, sir, Mr. Prime Minister," Elan said as he hung up the telephone.

He sat, taking deep breaths for a few minutes, and then he picked up the receiver and dialed 0.

His secretary answered.

"Send the two people who are waiting for me to my office," Elan said.

"Yes, Mr. Amsel."

Janice walked in with her husband beside her. She could not meet Elan's eyes. The years of lying and denying her past were now meeting her face-to-face. Here was Elan, the man she'd once thought she loved and the same man she had once thought she hated. He was the father of her child, and he was an arrogant, inconsiderate Israeli. However, Elan Amsel was the only thing that stood between her precious daughter and disaster.

Janice realized that at that moment, she was glad Elan was the strongest man she'd ever known. If there were a wall, he would break through it head-first. Yes, it was true. Elan had been a terrible husband, but there was no doubt that he was a magnificent soldier.

"It's been a long time," Elan said. "Come on in, both of you, and sit down."

Janice and Lucas sat in two chairs facing Elan, who sat behind his desk.

There was a long silence.

"I'm Lucas, Janice's husband," Lucas said, stretching his hand out to shake Elan's hand.

Elan did not return the gesture, and awkwardly, Lucas withdrew his hand.

"You are the man who raised my daughter?" Elan asked.

"Yes, I did. I love her as if she were my own child. She is a wonderful girl."

"Hmmm," Elan said, rubbing his chin and nodding as if he were going over everything again in his mind. "And the two of you, together, decided to keep my flesh and blood child from me for all these years?"

"Elan, I'm sorry. It was a mistake." Janice turned away from Elan and gazed out the window at Tel Aviv. The memories of her last morning in that city came flooding back to her. "I was so angry at you for leaving me and going to war. Elan, I'm sorry. But the mistake is on me. Blame me. But please don't let anything happen to Bari because of what I did."

"When we married, I told you I would put Israel first if Israel ever needed me. You should have understood that. I made it clear. That is what it means to be an Israeli."

"I didn't understand then, Elan. I was young. Please, I need your help. Bari needs your help. She's your child, Elan. She's your blood…" Janice was crying.

Elan leaned back in his chair and shook his head. Bari. Who the hell was Bari? He wished he had known her all these years. To him, she was a stranger. And now, this girl, this child of his own blood, was being held hostage by enemies of his beloved country.

"Have you met with the parents of the other girl who is missing?" Elan asked, trying to break the tension in the room.

"Not yet. We left our suitcases at the front desk. We haven't even been to the hotel yet. But we will see them as soon as we leave here."

Elan got up from behind his desk and walked to the window. He looked out for several minutes, then turned back to look at Janice and Lucas and sighed. "What's done is done. I can't change the past. But I am not going to allow a terrorist group to take the lives of two Jewish kids. So, you can count on me to do my best."

"She wanted to meet you," Lucas said. "She wanted a relationship with you. She's good and kind. I know it must be hard for you to take all of this in right now, but we appreciate everything…"

Elan raised his hand to stop Lucas from talking. "Enough." Elan's voice was firm. "I said I will do what I can."

"Thank you so much, Elan," Janice said.

"Go now." Elan waved his hand at Lucas and Janice. "I'll have my secretary keep you posted on any new developments," Elan answered, then sat down again at his desk, indicating that the meeting was over.

After they had left, Elan got up and closed the door to his office. He needed time alone. He had been slighted, but he'd decided to do his best to rescue the daughter that had been kept a secret from him all these years. His gut was churning. His feelings were so conflicted. It was a good time for a drink, something to calm his nerves, something to ease his anger.

CHAPTER THIRTY-ONE

Tova had finished her coffee before she went back into the interrogation room. She knew she was right about Gerhard, and the message that had been delivered from the FPN confirmed her suspicion. Gerhard was innocent. A group of terrorists had kidnapped the girls.

"You're free to go," Tova said to Gerhard. "We had some information come in, and we now know you had nothing to do with this."

"Thank you." Gerhard stood up and stretched. "I mean, really, thank you."

Tova looked at him. He was disheveled. She was a good judge of character. If she had no other gifts, she could usually rely on her intuition when it came to people. After the first half hour of questioning Gerhard, she believed he was telling the truth about everything he'd told her.

"So, you want to take me to lunch, and maybe we can talk about your meeting with Demjanjuk—a supervised meeting, of course," Tova said. It was lunchtime, and she was hungry. Was she being unconventional? Perhaps. But he was an innocent man, and something about him stirred her maternal instinct.

In many ways, he was like a child, weak and very unlike the Israeli men she knew. She had an hour for lunch, and he said he hated eating alone. That was why he'd asked the girls to dinner the night before. She was tired of eating alone, too. So why not?

"Yes. Yes, I do. I do want to talk about arranging a meeting. I would be so pleased if you let me take you for lunch," Gerhard said.

They walked quietly to a nearby diner. It was a simple place. They ordered food at the counter and sat at a white Formica table with two uncomfortable chairs.

"So, really? I can't believe that you came all the way to Israel to talk to this guy, this Nazi?" Tova asked, dipping her pita in the thick, white Tzatziki sauce.

"Yes, all the way from Germany. I've been struggling with this situation of mine for many years now. You see, my beloved father, the man I knew anyway, was a good and kind man. So, it's hard for me to believe he could have been a monster. Can you understand my shame? My dilemma?"

She nodded her head.

"He was such a gentleman at home, always so good to my brother and me. He treated my mother kindly and respectfully. At least, that is how I remember him. When I found out what he did when he left us and went to work during the day at the concentration camp, I was stunned. I am still stunned.

"For years, I searched for someone who might have known my father. I met with a Jewish man who was a survivor of the camp. He tried not to think about it, but he said that he remembered my father. When I told him who I was, my father's son, he spit in my face and said my father was a sadist.

"I was sick to my stomach. The meeting had solved nothing for me. The man left me sitting on a park bench. I watched him walk away, and then I ran home. It was about two miles, but I couldn't stop running. It was like if I could run fast enough, maybe I could escape from the past. But I couldn't outrun it... Do you understand?

"There was no place to go, no place to hide. My father's sins were all over me, covering me, smothering me. They still are and always will be. Every day, I awaken with guilt beyond measure."

"You have no reason to be guilty. You didn't commit the crimes; he did."

"Yes, but he was my father. I always wanted a family, but I will never have children because I know the bloodline must stop with me."

Tova hated Nazis. She knew plenty of survivors. They were all over Israel, and she'd heard their horrific, painful stories of being tortured by unscrupulous sadists.

She had friends and parents of friends who were still marred by the experiments that were done on their bodies. Tova had seen lots of frightening black and white photographs that had been taken of the piles of corpses, of the gas chambers, and the crematoriums.

And always, in the back of her mind, as in the back of the mind of every Jew, she knew that if she had been born in Europe during the reign of Hitler's Third Reich, her body and the bodies of her sisters and her parents would be amongst those skeletal corpses. So why did she not hate the man who sat across from her? How was it so easy for her to forgive him for the sins of his father?

"When I heard Demjanjuk was captured, I knew I had to talk to him. You see, I was just a little boy, but he came to my house once to meet with my father. I am sure I must be insane for doing this, but I must ask him if it is true. I have to hear the truth from his lips. I have to know for absolutely certain that my father really did these things, and if he did, why? I must hear it directly from someone who knew my father, another Nazi guilty of the same horrible sins…" Gerhard was not able to eat. His hands were shaking.

Tova was surprised at her reaction. She felt sorry for Gerhard. He was unlike any of the men she had ever known. He sat across from her, running his trembling hands through his thinning blond hair and looking like a broken marionette. Most men Tova grew up with were Israelis: strong-willed, unbending, and ashamed of weakness. This man, this Gerhard, seemed more vulnerable than a child. She watched him as he spoke of the anguish that haunted his soul, and Tova could not help but believe his words.

"I can't guarantee anything. I am only an officer of the law. However, I will try to arrange a meeting. It will be chaperoned, of course, and it will be through a glass. There will be no physical contact between you and Demjanjuk. You realize this?"

"I understand. If it could be arranged..."

"I'll see what I can do. Give me your hotel phone and room number, and I'll call you later this afternoon."

"Tova, thank you."

She nodded. He was a strange man, indeed.

———————

Tova put in a request to speak with her supervisor, who immediately called her into his office.

"What's this about?" he asked.

"You remember that German guy I questioned about the kidnapping case?"

"Yeah."

"Well..." She proceeded to explain why Gerhard had come to Israel and how she felt he should be allowed to meet with the old Nazi.

Her boss was appalled, and her request was denied. From the look on his face, she knew that there was no point in trying to convince him. The meeting between Gerhard and the Nazi, who was nicknamed 'Ivan the Terrible' because of the horrific things he did to the prisoners, would never take place.

After work, Tova walked home in silence through the busy streets of Tel Aviv. The delectable fragrance of food being prepared wafted out of the doors of the cafés and restaurants. Cars honked their horns. Women walked by, carrying bags filled with purchases. To Tova, everyone seemed to be in a hurry, and they all seemed to have a place to go. But she was alone, as always, and she returned as she did every night to the small studio apartment she shared with her cat, Aya.

As usual, Aya was meowing loudly when Tova opened the door. It was mealtime. Tova poured the hard pebbles of cat food into a bowl and then refreshed Aya's water. The cat ate furiously—as if she'd been denied food for weeks when, in fact, she'd been fed earlier that morning. Tova loved Aya's appetite. She gave her a feeling of purpose. A living thing depended upon her. That was a reason to go on living.

The truth was that she was terribly lonely. She'd never been married and was now past the age of having children. She had friends at work, but they had families and rarely had time to spend with a spinster.

Once, several years ago, Tova had thought about adopting a child. She relished the idea of being a mother, but then reality set in. She lived alone, and she had been able to save very little money over the years. Every paycheck counted. Therefore, she couldn't take time off of work. If she were even approved for adoption, there would be no one at home every day to care for the child. So, she'd abandoned the idea.

Tova changed into a pair of loose jeans and a T-shirt and then twisted her hair into a ponytail. She sat on the sofa and thought about what to have for dinner. There wasn't much food in the refrigerator.

She'd meant to go shopping, but shopping and cooking for one was depressing, so often she went without eating dinner. Tonight could easily be one of those nights. Aya finished her bowl of food and leaped up onto her master's lap. Tova kissed Aya's head and began petting her.

She knew she would have to call Gerhard and tell him that she had not been able to get him approved for a meeting with the Nazi. Knowing what she did about his life, she had no doubt he would be disappointed and devastated. Well, what was the point of turning it over in her mind? She might as well get it over with.

Once she told Gerhard, Tova could turn on the television and lose herself in some movie. Tova gently placed Aya on the floor. She got up, poured herself a glass of wine, and took Gerhard's phone number out of her purse. Then she picked up the receiver and dialed the hotel.

A phone operator with a cheerful voice put her through to the room.

"Gerhard?"

"Yes…"

"This is Tova from the police station." She should have called herself Officer Ben-Levi, but for some reason, she felt more comfortable being on a less formal basis with this man.

"Yes, Tova. I'm so glad you called. Did you find out anything?"

"I'm sorry, Gerhard. I cannot arrange a meeting. I tried…"

There was silence for a few minutes. He gave a short laugh, trying to make light of the situation, but she could hear the hurt in his voice.

"I should have expected as much… It's okay. You tried. I appreciate everything you've done."

"Are you going home tomorrow?"

"Yes, I'll leave as soon as I can get a flight."

"This might sound a little crazy, but you came all this way. I mean, it was a long flight and all." She took a sip of wine. She couldn't believe she was doing this. "I mean… Would you, maybe, like to see a bit of Israel? Learn a little about our people. After all, you're here already…" She was unsure why she'd even asked him and felt foolish. Tova held her breath, waiting for Gerhard to answer.

"You know, I would like to do that. I don't really know much about Israel or about the Jewish people. I only know what I have studied and read in books, but I've had very little actual contact with anyone who is Jewish. All I know is that I have this guilt I carry and the anti-Semitic fear-based stories that I've heard."

"Anti-Semitism doesn't die easily."

"No, it doesn't. I'm sad to say that it's still very much alive in Eastern Europe."

"You don't feel any anti-Semitism at all? You can tell me. I won't judge you."

"I don't know what I feel. I don't feel hatred. But the truth is that because I was raised with warnings about Jews, there are still some fears inside of me. But I want to dispel those fears. I want to go forward with my life and leave everything my father did and everything that society taught me behind. Does that make sense?"

"Of course. Why don't you get ready so I can show you a little Israel before the sun goes down?"

"I'd like that."

Tova picked Gerhard up at his hotel forty-five minutes later. She drove to Rothschild Boulevard and parked across the street from a white stone building.

"This is Independence Hall. Here is where Israel became a nation. The Jews fought long and hard for this."

"I know. I studied Jewish history. It's funny how guilt makes you want to know and understand things. I wanted to learn about Jews. I wanted to know why they were so hated."

"And what did you find out?" Tova asked.

"Nothing that makes much sense. I don't know why they have suffered the way that they have. The only thing I can think of is fear. People start rumors and make up stories, then ignorant people believe these stories. Before you know it, you have a serious problem."

"Now that you're here in Israel and surrounded by Jews, what do you see? What do you think?"

"The truth?"

"Of course. What else?"

"You won't be mad?" he asked.

"I promise."

"I see people who are maybe a little too bold, maybe too demanding and coarse."

"Yes, we are that way. We don't play games or have time for games."

"Yes, and also, I see a strong people, a people who would no longer go willingly to a concentration camp," he said, his voice cracking, "and a people who will fight to keep their religion and race alive."

"And how does that make you feel?"

He shook his head and bit his lower lip. "Glad that Hitler was not able to destroy the entire Jewish race. Sick that my father was a participant.

"But at least I can see that from what happened to them, the

Jews have become strong. I see the flag with the blue Star of David everywhere I go. It reminds me of seeing the yellow star as a child sewn onto the clothing of the Jews. Except now, that star is imprinted upon a flag that flies high with the pride of a people who fought for their very existence. Everywhere I've gone since I've been here, I can see these people's love for this country."

"I could take you to talk to some survivors, but I think you already know what happened."

"Oh yes, I do, and if I could change it, I would."

The building that housed Independence Hall was closed, but they walked up the street anyway.

"And the hardest part for me is that even with everything I know, I can't help it. I love my father. I don't love the man who lived inside my father's body and helped to commit mass murder. But I never knew that man. I never even knew of his existence until my father died. The man I knew was a kind and gentle husband and father to my mother, brothers, and me."

She looked up at him. His eyes were watery, and she thought he might cry again.

"How can you love and hate someone at the same time?" he asked, shrugging his shoulders.

She shook her head.

"I am ashamed. So ashamed."

They walked in silence for several minutes.

"Gerhard, you can't change the past. And even if you had known what your father was doing, you could not have stopped him. You were only a child."

"But how do I assuage the guilt? How do I forgive my father and make amends to the people he harmed so greatly? Is there any way to hope to even ask for forgiveness for such terrible crimes?"

"Gerhard, if you had committed the crimes, perhaps there would be no forgiveness. But it was not you who did these things."

"I know that intellectually… but emotionally, well, I've developed stomach ulcers from trying to live with all of it."

"Have you ever considered volunteer work?"

"You mean like community service?"

"Yes, like that."

"I don't know what I could do."

"I have an idea." She looked up at him and smiled.

"Yes?"

"Why don't we stop and have dinner, and I'll tell you?"

"All right," he said, nodding, "all right."

She heard the hope in his voice, and it comforted her.

They saw the sign for a kosher pizza restaurant about half a block away.

"Pizza okay with you?" she asked.

"Sure."

They placed their order at the counter for a cheese and mushroom pizza, two colas, and an Israeli salad. Tova reached for her wallet, but Gerhard stopped her. "I insist," he said.

"But you paid for lunch."

"Please allow me…"

She shrugged her shoulders.

"Come on, it's only a pizza?"

She nodded her head. "Okay."

He paid, then they sat at a table in the back of the restaurant. It was getting late, and the dinner crowd had already left, leaving only a few other tables occupied.

Tova smiled at Gerhard. He couldn't help but think that although she was not beautiful in a classic sense, she was certainly very pretty when she smiled.

"What I am thinking is this: perhaps you could see if you might be able to offer to speak to groups of people who come from all over the world to tour the concentration camps?"

"You mean like a tour guide?"

"Yes…"

"I would have to be at the camp all the time. It would tear me to pieces. I would have to take even stronger sleeping pills at night."

The man at the counter called Tova's name to say that the food was ready. Gerhard jumped to his feet. "I'll get it," he said and brought the food to the table.

"I have another idea. This one might be even better," Tova said, placing a slice of pizza on a paper plate, putting it in front of Gerhard, and then serving herself.

"You are full of ideas tonight," he said, but not sarcastically. His smile was genuine, and she couldn't help but be touched by the sincerity.

"Have you ever been to Jerusalem?" she asked.

"No, I came straight here to Tel Aviv. This is the only place I've been in Israel."

"When do you have to be back in Germany?"

"I have three weeks before I must return to work, but once I got the news about the meeting, I was going to leave right away."

"So, you can stay?"

"Yes… I can."

"Hear me out. In Jerusalem, there is a Holocaust museum and a memorial called Yad Vashem. Have you heard of it?"

"Vaguely, yes."

"This might be a crazy idea. After all, you have a job and a life in Germany. But what if you came here once a year when you took your vacation and arranged to speak at Yad Vashem? What if you could tell your story to the visitors who came there, and maybe by helping people to remember and to understand, you could, in some small way, prevent this from ever happening again?"

Gerhard studied this strange woman who sat across the table from him. He had never felt so attracted to anyone. She was unlike any woman he'd ever known intimately, with her olive skin, dark hair, and onyx eyes. The more he knew her, the more he found her beautiful. It was not a beauty that one could see immediately, but once he discovered it, he saw her beauty was constantly growing. She was kind, sensitive, and brilliant. He loved the idea of doing something meaningful that might, in some small way, help him to undo the sins of his father.

"I love the idea. But considering who my father was and everything about me, do you think the people at the museum would want me to speak?"

"I think so. It would be for the good of everyone involved. I can't see why they wouldn't want you to speak." Suddenly, she felt reckless. Tova had never taken any time off work. She'd worked with the police for twenty years and had never had a vacation.

The real reason she'd never gone anywhere was that she had nowhere to go and no one to go with. Her parents were long dead, and she had no siblings. The men in her life came and went, but she'd never had a serious relationship. "Would you like me to come with you to Yad Vashem? Perhaps I could help you explain what you would like to do?"

He cocked his head to a side, and his smile grew wide. "Yes, I'd like that very much."

"I'll go to work tomorrow and see if I can take a week off. Then, we can go to Jerusalem," she said. Tomorrow, she would ask the couple who lived in the apartment next door if they would watch Aya for a week. She could offer to pay them. Tova knew the woman fairly well; they talked in the laundry room every Sunday. The woman loved cats and had two of her own. Tova was fairly certain that she would agree.

CHAPTER THIRTY-TWO

THAT NIGHT, he felt lighter than he'd felt since he had made the terrible discovery about his father. If he could redeem himself by helping, even in some small way, to prevent another Holocaust, he would have found a purpose for his wretched life. He took a hot bath, and for once, he didn't think about his disastrous marriage or lonely apartment.

In fact, his mind was on the future and the strong Israeli woman who was willing to help him. He liked her. It had been years since Gerhard had even thought about being with a woman in a romantic sense. But she'd touched him with her kindness, understanding, and that miraculous strength that he found in most Israelis. Tova Ben-Levi—he even liked the sound of her name.

They spoke to each other in broken English, but it was enough for them to understand everything the other said and felt. Gerhard wondered if she had a husband or a boyfriend. She'd never mentioned it, and he'd never thought to ask. But if she were married, how could she go to Jerusalem with him for a week? And if she had a boyfriend, would her lover allow such a thing? Perhaps he was reading too much into all of this. Maybe she was just helping him, and he was the only one developing a romantic attraction.

Until Gerhard met Tova, he didn't realize how much he needed another person in his life, someone to share his deepest thoughts with. He'd become so used to being alone that he had accepted it as a way of life. Tova Ben-Levi—he loved the way her name sounded when he spoke it.

Gerhard was far too old to be acting like an infatuated schoolboy. But, as he lay in bed trying to fall asleep, he thought of how wonderful it might feel to abandon his conservative, constricting way of life in her arms. He considered how liberating it would be to murmur his need for her into her ear. Tova Ben-Levi, could you ever even consider falling in love with a man like me?

CHAPTER THIRTY-THREE

Tova turned the key to the door of her apartment. Aya immediately sprang out of her half-sleep, half-awake state of being and began to meow.

"You always hear me come home. I can hardly get in the house before you're here telling me all about your day," Tova said to her cat. Locking the door, she went to the kitchen with the cat following close behind her, rubbing Tova's calves with her soft fur. "Come on, my little friend. I know you missed me, so I am going to give you some treats. Yes, Mommy was out late tonight, and you're not used to Mommy going out after work. I'm so sorry."

Tova reached down to scratch Aya on the side of her cheek. "Would you believe I had dinner with a man? It's hard for me to believe, too. It's been years since I've been on a date. I thought that those days were over for me," Tova said. She took down the covered glass container where she kept Aya's cat treats and poured a small amount into her precious pet's bowl.

Aya's small teeth crunched the pebbles as Tova began getting ready for bed. Regardless of who his father may have been, there was no doubt that Gerhard Helmut was a good person. He was twisted up with guilt and tried very hard to do what he thought was right. Tova's instincts told her that he was sincere.

When she looked at him, she saw a middle-aged man who had probably once been very handsome. Now, his hair was thinning, and his features were probably not as chiseled as they had once been, but even so, Tova found him attractive. From his appearance, she assumed he was pretty close to the same age as she was, somewhere in his early fifties. He was very refined, soft-spoken, and so European.

She laughed out loud when she thought about that. Israelis were blunt and direct. She was used to people speaking loudly and arguing their opinions, sometimes without thinking first. Gerhard's strong desire to do something positive for Israel, to make up for his father's behavior, was admirable.

So many children and grandchildren of Nazis as well as young people who had the same ideology, still carried so much hatred in their hearts. They were raised to believe that Jews had no right to live, and that they were less than human. She was quite familiar with the anti-Semitic way of thinking.

But somehow, Gerhard was different. He had transcended all the teachings of his youth. He was trying. It was touching to see a man like that struggling to make every effort, somehow, to make right the wrongs of his father. Of course, no matter what he did, he would never be able to change the unforgivable things his father had done, but perhaps he, Gerhard, could make a difference. She couldn't help but like him. But she was hesitant to allow herself to see him romantically.

She'd been hurt so much by men through the years. When she was younger, there had been one-night stands but no real boyfriend and certainly no potential husband. Tova, a little too fat—Tova, not quite pretty enough—Tova, always the girl they left behind for someone better.

And still, even though she promised herself that she was through with men, Tova Ben-Levi was starved for love. Her body ached for the touch of another human being. It was not all about sexual need. She longed for someone to hold her hand, someone to hug her, and someone to sit on the sofa close enough that she could share his body heat.

No man had paid attention to her in at least ten years, and she craved the feeling of being held and wanted. Tova, Tova, she said out loud to herself. What are you thinking? Are you crazy? This man is from a Nazi father. This is certainly not someone you should be thinking of in this way.

But was he an enemy? Was he a Nazi? Was he really? He couldn't help who his father was or where he was born. Gerhard Helmut was born in Germany, the son of a Nazi SS concentration camp guard. Was it his fault?

If he could have chosen, she knew he would have chosen another path. But this was the path that he was destined to walk. It was not his decision, and now he showed great character in wanting to make things right. Tova smiled. She liked him. She liked him for his courage, for his kindness, for the heart that beat inside of him and was fighting to be a better man than his father was.

She tossed her clothes on the chair in her room, slipped on one of the long T-shirts she used as a nightgown, and hopped into bed. Aya was right behind her and leaped up gracefully, planting herself on the pillow next to Tova. Tova turned off the lamp next to the bed. She lay in the darkness thinking. Jerusalem…

Tova thought about traveling. She had not been to Jerusalem since she was a child. Well, she would only go if the neighbors agreed to take good care of Aya. She reached over and petted the cat's head. Aya meowed, a little annoyed at being disturbed as she fell asleep. Tova loved Aya like an only child. Tova leaned over and kissed Aya's head, and the kitty stretched into the position she'd slept in every night for the last seven years of her life. Then, Aya immediately fell asleep.

It was all arranged. It had been that easy. Tova was surprised that her neighbor had so readily agreed to watch Aya and even refused to take any payment. All she asked was that Tova would watch their cats when she and her husband traveled. That was an easy exchange. Tova loved cats. In fact, she loved all animals. Of course, she agreed. She would take care of her neighbor's pets.

When she got to work, she told her boss she wanted to visit some relatives and asked if she could have the rest of the week off. He didn't even try to discourage her. She left the office an hour after she'd arrived with a tingling excitement. Tova couldn't wait to tell Gerhard she would accompany him to Jerusalem.

Tova stopped at a clothing store for the first time in a long time. On most days, Tova window-shopped on her way home but never purchased anything for herself. Today, she bought the dress she saw in the window, a garment that was unlike anything she owned. The dress was a modern black spandex with huge shoulder pads; it was form-fitting and gave her an hourglass shape.

Next, she pulled into a market and purchased some over-the-counter hair color. It had been years since she'd even noticed how gray her hair had become. But today, she wanted to look her best. The first thing she would do when she arrived home was to apply the color, and then she would begin packing while the color processed. After her hair was shampooed, she would call Gerhard while it was drying. Then, she planned to deliver Aya to the neighbors and be on her way.

Gerhard answered the phone on the first ring.

"Hi, it's Tova. I have great news. I am off work for a week. I can go with you to Jerusalem."

She heard him take a deep breath and realized that he'd been waiting anxiously for her call. "That's great news. I'll rent a car," he said.

"I have a car. I'll drive."

"No, I don't want you to put miles on your car for me. I'll pay for a rental."

"Nonsense. This is my vacation, too. I insist on using my car."

"Very well, then. I insist on paying for all the gas and the hotel rooms." Then he cleared his throat in embarrassment. "Separate rooms, of course."

"Yes," she stammered. "Of course."

CHAPTER THIRTY-FOUR

BARI LYNN COULDN'T UNDERSTAND a word of what was being said upstairs. She only knew that her limbs ached, and her tailbone was sore from sitting in the same position for so long. Although she couldn't be sure, she thought they had been there for at least two days. Bari was terrified, more afraid than she'd ever been in her entire life.

Marilyn was constantly moaning and crying. The young man had come again with food and water. The next time he came, she decided that she would try to talk to him. Perhaps she could reason with him.

In the kitchen above the cellar where the girls were being kept, Athir and his brother Kazim were alone. The room was filthy. Guns of all sizes lay on the table, with ammunition in small cardboard boxes.

"I feel very uncomfortable about what we are doing with these girls. I think we should let them go," Athir said.

"And what about our brother? Do you ever want to see Fadi again?"

"Of course, but you know that keeping these girls like this is a mistake. It will bring us trouble. Now, not only Israel is involved, but America, too. Kazim, we are making a dangerous mistake. The Mossad will hunt us for the rest of our lives and kill us like dogs wherever they find us. Let them go."

"Athir, this is bigger than the two of us. We can't let them go. The entire organization would turn on us. They would kill us. We can't back out of this now."

"They are your friends more than mine. Talk to them. Tell them that we have gone too far this time. Tell them, Kazim, before it's too late."

"I think it is already too late."

It was several hours before Bari heard the cellar door creak open and Athir's footsteps descending the stairs. The wood creaked beneath his weight. Again, he carried a flashlight. He set the flashlight down on the floor, took the gun from his pants pocket, and held it with one hand.

"I brought food and water," he said. He untied her hands and handed Bari a water bottle and a handful of figs. She thought about fighting back, but he had a gun, and if she failed, both she and Marilyn would be dead. He untied Marilyn's hands and handed her a bunch of figs.

"Listen, there is no one around here to help you. My brother is upstairs."

Bari nodded.

The water was what Bari craved the most. Her throat was dry, and her lips were stuck together. She took the bottle and gulped half of it down. Then she handed it to Marilyn and decided it was time to try talking to Athir.

"Do you plan to kill us?" Bari asked, terrified of his answer.

"I don't want to do that. We are only trying to get our friends out of jail."

"Yes, but if they are not released, then what? Or even if they are, do you think this group of your friends is actually going to let us go?"

Marilyn was crying softly. Bari was terrified, but she was angry, too.

"My brother is the leader, and he promised he would let you go if we get our people back." The tone of his voice betrayed that he did not believe his brother. She could hear how conflicted he was.

"Can you live with yourself if they kill us and spill innocent blood?"

He did not answer. Bari was tempted to take her blindfold off so she could look into his eyes and reason with him, but she was mindful of his warning that it would mean certain death.

"Then why are you here? Why are you with them?" Bari asked.

"Bari," Marilyn said. "Stop. You'll make him mad… Then he'll do something to us."

"Why?" Bari insisted, ignoring Marilyn. "If you don't think this is right, why are you doing it?"

Athir shrugged his shoulders. "I don't know."

"Is that the best you can do? Is that your only answer?"

"Bari, please stop," Marilyn said.

"Because my brother is in jail, and I have to find a way to free him," Athir said, his voice was filled with anxiety. "My brother, who is in prison, and my other brother, who is upstairs, are members of the FPN. They both believe the only way for Palestinians to survive is by forming terrorist groups."

He called their group a terrorist group, not holy warriors or freedom fighters. It was not just talk, earlier when he said he was sorry. He does not agree with them.

"But aren't you a member of this FPN? Aren't you?"

"Yes," Athir said. "Reluctantly, but yes, I am."

"If you don't believe this is right, how can you be a part of it?"

"It is about my blood, my family. I have to do my part."

"Where do you see this going? Is rotting in prison or being killed what you want?"

"Athir." A male voice came from upstairs. "Why are you down

there so long? Make sure they are tied up tightly and come upstairs." It was Kazim.

"Hurry and finish your food so I can bind your hands."

The girls quickly finished off the figs and handed the empty water bottle back. "Thank you," Bari said, trying to hide the emotion in her voice. She felt the tears forming under her eyelids. She could very well die here in this terrible place. It was more than possible. When she kissed her mother and Lucas goodbye at the airport in Chicago, she had no idea it might be the last time she would ever see them.

It was funny. Meeting her birth father didn't matter anymore, and neither did the rejection from Ido. All Bari wanted was to go home to see her mother and Lucas. Lucas raised her; he was her real father. She longed to lie on the sofa in the living room and watch sitcoms, to eat pizza and drink cola, and... Please, God, let me go home to America. My mother was right. I don't belong here in Israel.

"We're only eighteen," Bari said. "Please, let us go... Please don't let them kill us."

"Athir?" Kazim called again.

"I'll be up in a minute. I am tying them up now."

"Come upstairs, and don't be sitting down there talking to the prisoners. The last thing you need is to start making friends with them. Get upstairs now."

"I'm sorry," Athir said, and he bound Marilyn's hands. "I really am sorry. I don't want to hurt you."

"I believe you," she said, and she wanted to believe. Dear God, how she wanted to believe.

When Athir went upstairs, his brother Kazim was waiting for him with Abdul and Muhammad.

"Come, we are going to pray," Muhammad said, and bent to lock the cellar door.

Athir and the others followed him. But Athir could not get the girls out of his mind. He knew in his heart that what they were doing was not right. His brothers were right that the Jews had stolen their land, and he wanted it back. Of course, he did, but not at the expense of two innocent girls.

Wouldn't it be wonderful if the Jews and Muslims could live side-by-side? Athir thought. *I've always been such an idealist. I doubt that could ever happen. There is too much anger, too much hatred.* He had secretly read the Old Testament of the Bible. He was always the seeker. He wanted to know more about Judaism. And the funny thing was that he learned that Judaism had similar references to his own religion. It was all so confusing.

All this death and destruction of people was not as it should be. If he looked at things from an unbiased standpoint, Athir knew that the Jews took the land along the Gaza Strip because they were being threatened. He didn't agree with what Israel did, but he understood it.

They'd seized the land during a war that should never have occurred. At least, that was Athir's true belief. He could never tell his brothers his true feelings, especially now with Fadi rotting in prison, waiting for the FPN to do something to free him. His brothers had turned into angry and violent men.

The FPN wasn't the only terrorist cell. There were many, far too many. Athir was afraid to voice any opposition in front of the others. He tried to persuade Kazim to change his mind, but he only did that when they were alone. He had no doubt that the others would kill him if they knew his true feelings. And he knew he was not the only one who lived in fear.

"Athir, you are always daydreaming," Kazim said. "Come on. Let's go."

Athir followed his brother. "Have we gotten any response from America or Israel about releasing Fadi?" Athir asked.

"They say they need more time. Before they will consider releasing anyone, they want proof of life. We have to let them hear the girls' voices on the phone. They have a phone number where they want us to call. It is on all the television stations. They want us to call so they can hear the girls. Then they say that they will arrange something. I don't trust them, but we have no other choice if we want to see Fadi again. Before we call them, we are going to move the girls in case they are tracing the call. Then we'll telephone them and let them see that we have not killed the hostages."

"When is all of this going to take place?

"The beginning of next week. We had to arrange for a safe area where we could bring the girls to make the call. Then, of course, we will need to get them there. Once we hang up the phone, we must quickly move them to another location."

CHAPTER THIRTY-FIVE

GERHARD WAS BITING his lip and sweating as he and Tova came close to Jerusalem. Tova could see that he'd broken out in blotches on his face and neck. She knew it would be difficult for him to go to Yad Vashem and admit the sins of his father and then tell them what he wanted to do.

She glanced away from the road for a minute, reached over, squeezed his hand, and smiled at him. He mustered a smile back. Tova could not help but admire this sad man who had come from such a dark and terrible background. He could have turned his back on his past, but he was trying. She had to admire that.

They arrived at Yad Vashem.

"Do you want to go to the hotel and check in first? Maybe you would like to freshen up a little?" she asked him.

He did. He wanted to go away from the memorial. It made him nervous. Gerhard felt like he might vomit from anxiety. But he was afraid he might not find the courage to return if he left now.

"No, no, let's go in. Let's do it now," he said.

Tova nodded. "Okay."

He opened the door to the building for her, and they entered. Gerhard felt dizzy as he looked around him. This was what his father had done—his own father. He could barely take a deep breath. How was he ever going to explain to these people what he wanted to do and why? Could he expect anything but hatred from them toward him?

Gerhard stood back while Tova went to the front office and asked if they could see someone who could discuss volunteer work. Gerhard wished he was on a plane back to Germany as they waited in an office with bright fluorescent lights blurring his vision. Were the people here at Yad Vashem going to blame him? Was he going to be damned by them and ostracized for coming? His hands were shaking so hard that he could not keep them still.

"Come in," an old woman, short in stature, with dark hair sprinkled with gray, said to them.

Tova got up and took Gerhard's elbow. He was glad that she did because he wasn't sure that he could stand up on his own. They entered a small office with a plain brown wooden desk, three uncomfortable chairs, two for guests, and one behind the desk.

"Hello, I'm Malka Solomon," the woman said, extending her hand. Tova shook hands with her, and then Gerhard did as well, even though his hand was trembling and sweaty.

"I'm Tova Ben-Levi. This is my friend, Gerhard Helmut."

"German?"

"Yes," he said, his voice cracking.

Tova began. "Gerhard is from Germany. He wants to talk to you about something that has been pressing on him…" She felt foolish. She had no idea what to say. It must come from Gerhard, not from her.

He seemed to realize this. Clearing his throat several times, Gerhard said, "Mrs. Solomon. It was very difficult for me to come here. You see, my father…" He coughed. "My father was an SS officer."

The look on her face made him want to run, but he didn't. Instead, he forced himself to continue. He'd come this far. He could not leave without doing something about his guilt.

"Go on…" she said.

Then he saw the tattoo on her arm. "You were in Auschwitz?" he asked.

"Yes. My family died there. I am the only survivor."

"I'm sorry. I'm so sorry." Gerhard was unable to hold back the tears. He began weeping like a child. The years of guilt, of blaming himself, were now all bubbling like boiling water to the surface. "I've come here because of what my father did. I can't live with it. Since I found out who he was and what he did during the war, I have been racked with guilt. I can't go on this way. I must do something." His face was as red as ripe strawberries and wet with tears, and his nose was running.

"I met Tova, and I told her my situation. She suggested that maybe you would allow me to come here once a year and speak. I want to apologize for what my father did. Maybe I can do something, something, anything… I know that no apology can bring your family back or any of the others who died—not the women, the children, or the poor, innocent people who were murdered… My God, you have no idea how sorry I am…"

"But you were only a child." Malka Solomon said. "You didn't do anything."

"He was my father. I have his blood running through my veins. I've even had myself sterilized, so I don't carry on the bloodline. That was all I could do…"

"Did you want children?" Malka asked.

"Yes, I would have loved to be a father. My decision to be sterilized cost me my marriage, but I had to do it." He wiped his nose with the back of his hand. "I had no choice. What if the cruelty or mental illness that had to be somewhere inside of my father for him to do what he did showed up in my child?"

"You think your father was mentally ill?"

"A person would have to be deranged to do something like this."

"And you are afraid that you might also be mentally ill?"

"Of course, I am afraid. But I know that I could never kill or hurt anyone."

"So, you want to come to Yad Vashem once a year and speak?"

"Yes."

"It won't be easy. There will be people who will hold your father's crimes against you. You do understand this?"

"Yes."

"I realize that you want to help, to redeem yourself for your father's actions. But the truth is that you are not responsible."

"I feel responsible. I feel I need to do this," he said.

"The audience who comes to listen to you could very well say hurtful things. I want to make sure that you understand this. You will be putting yourself in a position for criticism."

"Yes, I do. I understand."

"We won't be paying you. This is strictly volunteer work."

"I realize this."

"All right. Then we will put together a program and a time for you to come once a year to speak," Mrs. Solomon said. "I don't know anything about your schedule. I am assuming you will be coming from Germany. This will cost you a lot of money."

"Yes, I know. I am willing to spend the money."

"Then talk to my secretary and tell her when the best time is for you. She will make the necessary arrangements."

"I don't have much to offer, I am afraid. But please accept a small donation." Gerhard took his wallet from his pocket and laid a few bills on the desk.

"Thank you for your generosity," Malka said.

Tova watched Gerhard. He was an amazing man.

Tova and Gerhard rode to the hotel in silence. They checked into separate rooms. It was two hours before Tova knocked on Gerhard's door. He opened it and smiled.

"Do you want to go and get something to eat? I'm starving," she said.

"That's a good idea."

They walked for half a block and then found seats at a café. After they had placed their order, Gerhard handed the menus to the waitress.

"Thank you for coming with me today, Tova. I couldn't have done it alone."

"You were very brave."

"Was I? I don't know. I wish that I could do something more. I wish I could somehow change the past, change my father's actions."

"I know you do, Gerhard, but you can't. We have no control over what our parents did or didn't do. My father had a terrible temper. He hit my mother. I was just a child. What could I do? I cowered in the corner. That was all I could do. Finally, he beat her so badly that she had to be hospitalized. I blamed myself for not stopping him. But how could I? I was only ten years old."

"You couldn't…" he said.

"And you couldn't control your father any more than I could control mine."

They were silent for several minutes. Then the food arrived. Tova made up a sandwich with hummus and chicken, but she couldn't eat it. She took a bite and was unable to swallow. After she spit the mouthful into the napkin, she looked at Gerhard with tears in her eyes.

"I'm sorry. I didn't mean to be disgusting at the table."

He shrugged. "Is something wrong with the food?"

She took a trembling breath of air. "My mother committed suicide. I found her on the bathroom floor in the morning when I got up to go to school."

"Oh my God! Tova, I'm sorry."

"I never told anyone this. Before she killed herself, my mother left my father. We moved in with my aunt and her husband. They had two children, a boy and a girl, both a little older than me.

"My mother was very depressed. Even with how my father treated her, she missed him. I tried every way a ten-year-old could to make it up to her. I thought I could be everything to her—a daughter and a best friend, you know? I could make her happy enough to forget my father. I brought home excellent grades on my papers from school, but she just smiled and patted my head. 'That's very good, Tovala,' she would say.

"I saved my lunch money and bought her dried figs. She loved them. I thought maybe it would make her happy. But again, she said with a sad smile, 'Thank you so much, my Tovala.' She called me 'Tovala.'"

"Oh, Tova. What can I possibly say to make you feel better?"

Tova shrugged. "We went back to my father. For a while, he was all right. Then, one day, he beat her again. This time was worse than ever. Again, we went back to my aunt's house."

"She was beyond unhappy. She lay in bed all day without getting up or getting dressed. She stopped taking showers. I didn't know which was worse: the depression she suffered when she was away from my dad or the beatings.

"I remember trying to pretend that everything would be all right. In fact, I made up a fantasy in my mind. I had a dream life that existed in my head. In this dream, my father came back, but this time, he was different. He was loving. He told my mother that he realized he'd made a mistake and had changed. Now my mother was happy. This fantasy helped me to go on with my life.

"I can still remember going to school with my cousins, forcing the reality of what my mother was going through my mind as I played on the playground."

Gerhard reached for her hand. She allowed him to place his hand on top of hers. "I'm so sorry, Tova," he said.

"When I found her, I was sickened, but the truth was that I wasn't surprised. I was terrified, heartbroken, alone, and worst of all, maybe even a little relieved." She looked away. "I can't believe I just admitted that to you. But I hated to see her miserable every day, miserable, and more miserable…"

"It's okay. I understand. I am glad that you feel you can talk to me. I feel the same way about you. Would you like to leave?"

"You haven't finished your food," she said.

"I don't care."

"Yes, I would like to go, please."

Gerhard tossed more than enough money to cover the bill and the tip on the table. Then they walked outside. Tova leaned against the building and bent over to catch her breath. Gerhard put his arm under her elbow, and they walked back to the hotel together.

When they arrived, Gerhard went to Tova's room. He was afraid to leave her alone. She'd just relived a terrible memory, and he was not sure she could be trusted not to hurt herself.

"Let me order some wine from room service. Maybe it will help to calm your nerves," he said.

"I think I am going to take a hot bath," she said.

"Maybe you should wait a little while, Tova. Let's just sit here together. Would that be all right with you?"

She looked at him. He was such a kind and gentle soul. How could his father have been such a terrible man? But she, too, was a kind and gentle soul, and wasn't her father a terrible man?

"Yes, I'll sit with you."

"Tova..."

"Yes?"

"I like you. I mean, I like you very much. You are a special woman..."

She gave a harsh laugh. "Special?"

"Yes, special. You are beautiful, understanding, and warm."

"Beautiful? I highly doubt that..." She laughed again. It was a bitter laugh.

"I mean what I am saying, Tova."

There was a knock at the door. It was room service. Gerhard tipped the delivery man and signed the bill. After he had closed the door, he poured a small glass of red wine for Tova and another for himself.

"We should only drink a little. We haven't eaten much today," he said.

"I can drink and not eat. I've done it plenty of times," Tova said.

They sipped the wine.

"I like you too, Gerhard. You're a deep thinker, and you feel things deeply, too, like me."

"I'm glad." He smiled. "Tova?"

She cocked her head to the side.

"Can I kiss you?"

She nodded. "Yes."

Slowly, he moved closer to her. Then, tenderly, he took her head in both hands and moved his face to hers. He nibbled her lips at first and then devoured them with passion. She let out a small sigh of passion from a need that had been suppressed for many years.

He inhaled the clean scent of her shampoo as she moved closer into his arms. His heart fluttered, and the desire rose within them both.

Gerhard stood up and extended his hand. Tova arose and put her hand in his. Then he led her to the bed. Gerhard abandoned himself to his need for this woman who had captured his heart with her understanding. With gentle hands, he peeled her clothes away. Then he stood and removed his own.

"Are you all right?" he asked.

"Yes," she whispered. "I want you…"

They made love slowly and tenderly for an hour. When it was over, Tova lay in Gerhard's arms. The room was silent except for the sound of their breathing.

"You are beautiful, no matter what you say…" he said.

She didn't answer, but she was smiling in the darkness.

He cradled her closer to him. The warmth of her skin against his own filled the most basic human need: the need to be loved.

Neither spoke for several long minutes.

"I had a breakdown," Gerhard said. "After my wife left me, I couldn't eat or sleep. I stayed with my brother and his family for two months until I could get back on my feet."

"Did you go to work?"

"No, I couldn't. I took time off. My boss understood, thank God. You know Tova, I never told anyone about this. I dated a few women since my divorce, but never more than a few dates. They were nice ladies, but I never felt anything towards them. In fact, when I was with them, I felt more alone than when I was alone. Does that make sense?"

"Yes, more than you know. I spent much of my life chasing love." She gave a harsh laugh. "The harder I chased it, the faster it ran away from me. Every man I thought I might be able to care for walked away from me."

"You've never been married."

"Never."

"Have you ever been in love?"

"No, not really. I mean, there were men I wanted to be in love with because I wanted to have a family and a home of my own. But I can't say that I truly loved them."

He leaned down, kissed the top of her head, and squeezed her shoulder. "You are a remarkable woman, Tova Ben-Levi, a woman like I have never known before in my life."

Again, there was silence for several minutes.

"My father taught me to whittle." He smiled into the darkness as he recalled the memory.

"You mean to carve wood?"

"Yes. You know, to make things out of wood. When I was in my teens, I made an entire chess set out of wood. Of course, my father was dead by then. But I made the chess set in honor of his memory. For me, it was a way to still feel close to him even though he was gone. It's crazy, right? Anyway, the set was perfect, every piece a work of art."

"That's impressive."

He laughed. "The funny thing or the terrible thing, depending upon how you look at it, is that I love him. I can't help it. I know what he did, yet I still love him somehow. I hate what he did, but he was my father."

"I know. I really understand."

"I know you do, Tova, and that might be one of the reasons I think I am falling in love with you."

No one had ever said those words to her before. Tova felt her heart swell, and the tears began to form behind her eyes. In her lonely life, she'd always kept a secret dream, the dream of a man speaking of love to her.

When she was young, she'd even had years of promiscuous sex in hopes of finding that special someone who would see beyond her plain face and ordinary body. She'd dreamed of that one person who would say, "Tova, you are my one and only." But it had not happened and finally, she'd given up.

She'd resigned herself to a life dedicated to work and caring for her precious Aya. That was until she'd met Gerhard. Now, in the most unexpected of men, she'd found him, the man she'd searched for her entire life. God did his work in very strange ways.

Tova could not speak.

"I hope I didn't scare you by saying that I think I am falling in love with you," he said.

"No, no."

"I didn't mean to scare you away."

"You didn't. I care for you, too, Gerhard. Very much. Very much…" The words hurt her throat because they were so filled with real emotion.

"Marry me. Come to live with me in Germany. I have a nice home. You will like it. In fact, I have a rose garden. It's my hobby. Roses of all colors…"

"Germany?"

"Yes, it's been a long time since the war. Jews are not in any danger in Germany anymore."

"Gerhard." She took a deep breath. She might be falling in love with him, but… "Gerhard, I am an Israeli. I was born here, and this is my home. Israel is my land, and this is my way of life."

"You don't think you could love me?"

"I think that maybe I already do love you." She felt the pain of loss in the pit of her stomach, but she knew that what she was about to tell him was the only truth she could live with. "Gerhard, I'm sorry. I cannot leave here. I can never leave here. Israel is forever my homeland."

CHAPTER THIRTY-SIX

BARI LYNN HADN'T REALIZED she was holding her breath until the door to the underground room closed, leaving Bari and Marilyn alone again. She wasn't afraid of the boy who brought the food and water. She was certain he was not as cruel as the others in his group. But whenever the door creaked open, Bari's heart began to race. It could be the boy again, or it might be the last breath she and Marilyn would take.

Her skin itched, and she wondered if it was from nerves or insects. When Athir had removed her bonds to go pee, she felt her arm breaking a spider's web. She didn't tell Marilyn. She would become hysterical if she knew there was a spider in this cellar.

She'd heard some buzzing in her ear a few times and wished her hands were free to swat away the insects. At least she and Marilyn could talk to each other. That was a blessing, something to be thankful for in the middle of this trip to hell.

Bari heard several harsh voices upstairs, raised in anger. She thought that the language they were speaking was Arabic. All Bari could understand was the tone, but that was enough to tell her that there was dissension amongst their captors.

But it seemed that the heated discussions were only between

Athir and the one he called Kazim. The voice of Kazim also spoke to the others with authority. *He must be the leader, and Athir is not afraid to argue with him when they are alone. He said one of them was his brother. That's it, Athir must not be afraid of him because he is his brother.*

Was this a good or bad thing for her and Marilyn? Bari had no idea. It was unnerving to listen to arguments that might determine her life or death and not to understand a word that was spoken.

"Are you hurt at all?" Bari asked Marilyn as she leaned against her.

"No. I mean, my hands hurt where they are tied together, my legs are asleep, and I can hardly sit anymore because my tailbone is aching. But otherwise, I think I'm okay. Bari, do you think we'll get out of this alive?"

"I don't know. I heard Israel doesn't negotiate with terrorists, but I'm unsure about America."

"I'm so scared, Bari. I wish I'd never come here."

"Me, too. My mom was right. She hated Israel. She knew something bad was going to happen to me if I came here. And it did." Bari couldn't hold back anymore. She began crying. "I wish I could just go home."

"Me, too. I keep thinking about that guy in the wheelchair that the terrorists threw off the cruise ship a year ago. Do you remember? It was all over the news. My dad talked about it all the time."

"I remember something about that, but I wasn't really paying attention. I think I can remember my parents talking about it a little. It happened somewhere in the Mediterranean. I'm not sure, but I think it was the PLO. They took control of a cruise ship, and they threw this old guy in a wheelchair off the deck and into the water, and he died. He was Jewish. It was terrible."

"Is that the same group who has us right now, the PLO?" Bari asked.

"No, he said the FPN. I am really scared. I can't believe that this is happening to us."

"Yeah, I know. I can't, either. I feel like it's a horrible nightmare, and I will wake up. Except it's real, and I'm here, and you're here."

"What are we going to do?" Marilyn asked.

"The only thing we can do. We have to try to make that boy feel sorry for us. Maybe he'll be able to talk his friends into letting us live."

"Do you think so?"

"Who knows? It's not like we have any other options. I keep telling myself that Israel, America, my dad, or even my Israeli dad will somehow step in. Still, nobody seems to be doing anything at all. The guys upstairs sound so angry all the time. I wish I could understand what the hell they were saying," Bari said.

"I wish your dad would come and save us. Everyone knows that he is a master martial artist."

"Yeah, me too. But how would he ever find us? They have us buried in this underground cavern. I don't think anybody can find us."

"Didn't your father teach you karate?"

"Yeah, he's a sixth-degree black belt. He's been teaching me since I was really young. I know what to do, but I'm afraid to try to fight. This isn't a movie. There are a lot of them. They have guns and weapons, and I'm worried that if I try to fight back and I don't win, they will go crazy, and they could really hurt us."

The door creaked open. Bari said a silent prayer that it was Athir. She leaned against Marilyn, who leaned back against her. If it was Athir, she would try to make light talk and maybe find some way to get him to empathize with them. If she could just reach him, somehow convince him that she and Marilyn were human beings just like him, they deserved to live. He was the only one of their captors who seemed to know right from wrong.

Being in the darkness for so long without sight, her ears had become extremely sensitive. The footsteps on the wooden stairs were much heavier than Athir's. The first set of steps was followed by two more. It sounded like more than one person was coming down. Bari shuddered.

A heavier, stronger man than Athir pulled Bari to her feet. Roughly, he threw her over to the other man and then did the same to Marilyn.

Bari felt the breath catch in her throat. She wanted to fight back, but she trembled with fear. The consequences could be grave. She couldn't take the risk, not now, not yet.

"Athir," the voice of Kazim yelled. Then, he spoke angry words in Arabic to the others.

"Please…" Marilyn said, whimpering.

The man hit her across the face, and her lip began bleeding. Marilyn screamed. Athir came running down the stairs.

"Do you think they are taking us to kill us?" Marilyn asked Bari, sobbing.

"Shhhh…" Bari whispered.

"Shut up," Kazim said harshly, in English. "Don't say another word, or I'll kill you both."

Kazim was pointing to Bari's mouth. He picked up some duct tape and threw it at Athir. "We're taking them, now. Tape their mouths shut."

"I'm sorry," Athir said in English, so Bari knew he was speaking to Marilyn and herself. Then he taped Bari and Marilyn's mouth. One of the men nudged Athir and then shook his head in disgust.

The tape across her lips made Bari feel like she was suffocating. It was hard to calm down enough to remember how to breathe through her nose. She was hyperventilating, drawing air quickly and violently as if she might be denied the privilege of breathing at any moment.

"Let's go," Kazim said in Arabic. "You two, move quickly."

Bari and Marilyn were surrounded on both sides by the terrorists. She perceived that they had gone through the front door to the street and heard motor noises and the sounds of children playing at a distance. As she was forced into the street, Bari felt the terror shoot through her entire body. She began to tremble uncontrollably. Someone hit her with the butt of a gun. She could not see who it was that delivered the blow. Then she heard Athir arguing with the others in Arabic.

Please, please, Athir, don't leave. You are the only small chance Marilyn and I have of surviving this ordeal.

One of the terrorists pushed the girls forward. Bari almost lost her balance, but she recovered, and the two girls were herded into a vehicle. She thought it was a small bus of some kind because she tripped on a stair entering and felt the metal pierce her shin. The pain only reinforced her fear as the vehicle began to move. Bari wondered where the terrorists were taking them and why. The feeling of total vulnerability was devastating.

Without being able to see or understand the language, Bari had no inkling of what to expect. She could not see or hear Marilyn, so she wasn't even sure her friend was still beside her.

Bari estimated the driving time at over an hour. Then, if things couldn't possibly get more terrifying, they did when the vehicle stopped. Bari still had no idea if Marilyn was with her. She only knew she was pushed headfirst out of the bus, landing on her face in what seemed like dirt or sand. She felt the grit against the skin of her cheek.

There was a stirring around her. She heard something that sounded like a blow, but she could not be sure who had been hit or even if someone had been struck. She hoped that Marilyn was all right.

A rough hand pulled her to her feet and then pushed her forward. She wished that she could speak, that she could ask Athir what was going to happen. But the tape covering her lips forbade her from making any sound. She wasn't even aware that her tears were soaking the blindfold and couldn't help but wonder if this was where the terrorists were bringing them to kill them.

They walked only a few feet and then entered an enclosure of some kind. The street noises stopped, the sun no longer on her cheek, and Bari could smell strange spices. Her heart pounded so hard that she felt like she might have a heart attack. Again, the rough hands were upon her shoulder, forcing her painfully into a chair. She felt the hard base of the chair against her tailbone.

A conversation in Arabic took place between Athir and Kazim. Marilyn and Bari could not see anything and were terrified of what might happen next.

"I will remove the tape from your mouths in a few minutes. Please, I am begging you not to scream. I don't want these men to hurt you." It was Athir.

"I'm sorry. Please, just do as you are told. Please don't ask any questions. You are in terrible danger…" Athir said. "Listen to me. We are here at this place because you must make a phone call. We are going to make this call to let the Israeli government know that you are still alive. You must not say anything except that you are alive and that you are both unharmed. Do you understand me?" Athir said to both Bari and Marilyn. "If you don't do as I tell you, they will kill you on the spot. Don't say anything other than what I am telling you to say. Please, it is for your own safety."

The girls both nodded their heads.

"If you say anything else—if you tell the Israelis anything else—the men here will hurt you. Please, just do as they ask…"

Again, the girls nodded their heads.

"Athir, you stay here! We will be right back. And you two girls, don't try anything stupid because if you do, I have no problem killing you. Do you understand? I will personally cut off your heads and hang them in front of the American Embassy." It was Kazim speaking.

The other terrorists left. Athir was alone with Marilyn and Bari. Bari knew this may be her last chance.

She could hear him pacing the room, and Bari felt that he was quite distraught. She hoped he was feeling guilty, a bit frightened, and perhaps worried enough about the consequences of letting her and Marilyn go.

"Athir, have you ever had dreams for your life?" Bari asked.

Athir was taken off-guard by the question. "I was accepted to go to medical school to be a doctor, he said, shaking his head."

"Where?"

"In America."

"You know, if you don't let us go, you will either be killed or go to prison. Even if you don't get arrested because of your associations, you will never get past the Terrorist Watch List to go to America, and you will never be a doctor."

"I know."

"The violence is wrong, but you can do your part to end it here and now," said Bari.

"The Israelis do something to us, then we do something to them, and then they do something to us," Athir said, seeming like he was talking to himself. "We kill some Israeli teenagers, and they kidnap and kill one of ours. So, then we bomb a police station. They capture several of our members, and we threaten to kill two innocent girls. Where does this end? How will this ever end?"

Because Athir was not convinced that what the terrorists were doing was right, the girls were hoping against all hope. Perhaps his conscience would force him to help them. The fact that Athir was so conflicted inside was a good thing.

Bari believed that, deep down, he was a good person who had become too deeply involved with the wrong group. What words could she say to convince him to let them go? And, if by the grace of God, he did free them, where were they? Bari could not be sure. They might be in the middle of the desert. If they were, how would they ever find their way out with no vehicle or water? How far was civilization, and in which direction should they walk?

"Athir," Bari said in a small voice. "Please, Athir, you are our only hope. Please let us go. Please help us to get home to our families. We aren't political. We are just two American girls who came to Israel to visit. Please, Athir."

He shook his head. "I can't. The Israelis have my brother. I have to help free my brother from jail." He sounded like he was trying to convince himself.

"Marilyn and I are only eighteen, Athir—just eighteen. How old are you?"

He shook his head but didn't answer. Instead, he kept pacing the room like a caged panther.

"We haven't had a chance to live yet, Athir. We have never been married nor had children of our own. Marilyn and I didn't do anything to you or your brother. We didn't do anything to anyone. Please, Athir, please. You are a good person; I can tell. Let us go. Just untie us and let us go. Do the right thing, Athir."

"Shut up. Shut up, right now," Athir cried out, covering his ears with his hands. He looked at Bari and then at Marilyn. It seemed as if he was going to untie them. Bari felt a glimmer of hope. If he freed them, they would find a way back. She wasn't sure how, but they would have a better chance than they did right now.

Her heart was thundering in her chest. *Untie us, Athir,* she thought. Please, Athir. By his silence, she felt that he was considering releasing them. But then the rest of the group burst through the door, and the moment was gone, lost forever.

Bari felt sadness like she'd never known before.

Five Arabic men were scattered around the room. One of the men plugged a thick, black desk phone into an outlet on the wall. They spoke to each other in Arabic as Marilyn and Bari were filled with panic. *Anything could happen*, Bari thought, *anything at all.*

The man in charge dialed the phone. He put it on speaker while the rest of the group gathered around him. He motioned to Athir with his hand, indicating that Athir should bring the girls closer.

Athir took Marilyn and Bari by the shoulders and brought them closer to the telephone.

Both girls were seated on the floor beside the phone. They heard the ringing.

"This is the FPN. We are calling you to give you what you asked for: proof of life," the man in charge said. "I've been told to speak to Elan Amsel. Put him on the phone immediately. I will not hold the line long enough for you to trace the call. So, hurry, or I will hang up."

Mossad had been awaiting this telephone call. The most modern tracing equipment was already in place and activated.

Elan Amsel? Bari felt her throat close as she gasped. Her father? Did they know that he was her father? Is that why she was kidnapped?

"This is Amsel," the heavy baritone voice came through the telephone receiver. Bari heard her father's voice for the first time. She felt as if she might cry. The entire scene was surreal to her.

"You know who we are and why we are calling. Speak," the thick man said to Marilyn. "Speak! State your name and tell the other party on the phone that you are alive."

In a small voice, Marilyn did as she was told.

"Now, you." He pointed to Bari.

"My name is Bari Lynn Allen. I am alive, and I am unharmed."

In the offices of Mossad, Elan Amsel's hand went to his heart. This was his child, his daughter, his blood. The terrorists didn't know. He was sure of that. But just hearing her voice made all of it real for him. He felt dizzy and sick with worry.

"You see. They are fine. So! Now, you have three days to release the prisoners, or they will no longer be fine. They will be dead," the leader said, smashing the phone down on its cradle.

Then he turned to the other terrorists. "Hurry, we have to get them back into the van and get out of here quickly, in case the call was traced. If it was, and the Israelis had our location, they'd be here in minutes. Hurry up," Kazim tersely repeated.

"Did you get a location on them?" Elan shouted to the men working with the tracing equipment.

"Hold on, sir, we're trying."

Elan felt his heart had stopped beating as he waited for what seemed like forever, but it was only seconds. He bit his lower lip, trying not to lose patience. He wanted to yell at his coworkers to tell them to move faster. But he knew they were experts, doing the best possible job.

"We lost them."

"Damn. How could you lose them?" Elan asked and sunk into the chair behind his desk. He reached for a flask inside the drawer in his desk, raised it to his lips, and then took a long swig. The whiskey burned his throat, but it brought him a moment's peace.

"They hung up before we could get a location."

"Son of a bitch." Elan banged his fist on the table.

"I'm sorry, sir. I tried."

"At least the girls are alive. Now comes the hard part. Somehow, we are going to have to find them..." Elan coughed. He didn't want to talk to Janice again, not yet. "You," he pointed to one of the younger Mossad agents. "Call the parents of both of the girls and tell them that we got proof of life."

"Yes, sir, Mr. Amsel. Right away."

Elan leaned back in his chair and rubbed his chin, his mind racing at a thousand miles an hour. Where could they be? The FPN was a well-known sect of the Fatah Al-Intifada. He knew all about them; it was his job to know. They were a violent group, like the PLO, and they would think nothing of killing the girls if their demands were not met.

Israel did not negotiate with terrorists. This was something every Israeli knew, and every Israeli lived with the possible consequences. But they also knew that once Israel began to give in to the demands of terrorists, the power of Israel would be lost.

There had to be a way to find the girls. Every spy employed by Mossad had been sent out to search for the Americans. They'd talked to members of the FPN and the PLO, but so far, they'd come up with nothing. This had to be a very small, select group. Elan thought there was a good chance that at least some of the kidnappers were related to the FPN prisoners they wanted to be released.

Think, Elan, think. Where could the FPN be keeping the girls? The problem with any of the Fatah was that they were so transient. They had caves and basements, cellars, and barns all over the Middle East. The girls could be anywhere, anywhere at all.

CHAPTER THIRTY-SEVEN

THE VAN SEEMED to fly through the streets, soaring over bumps in the road. Once, they hit a pothole so hard that Bari's head banged against the top of the vehicle.

Bari contemplated Athir's position and their plight. The people he cared most for, including his family, were involved. She and Marilyn were strangers. She was convinced they were within an inch of Athir letting them go before the rest of them came back. Her heart sank. There may not be another chance.

The van backed up. Bari's heart dropped. Where were they? The drive had not been so long this time. Was this a lonely road where she and Marilyn would be murdered? The door to the van flung open. They were in a different part of town than before; the sounds were different.

One of the men came and pulled Marilyn and then Bari by the shoulders, and both girls were forced out of the van. Then, without hesitation, they were directed into the building. This was a new location. The room smelled different, cleaner than before, and spices like someone had been cooking. The number of steps to the stairs was different, and the number of steps to the lower floor was ten more.

"Mahir." Kazim indicated that he was speaking to another one of the members. Kazim handed the man two long metal dog chains with collars attached.

The man called Mahir put the collars around Marilyn's and Bari's necks and then chained them to a thick metal pole in the center of the room.

"Oh no, please!" Marilyn said and began to cry.

What now? Bari's mind was racing. What now? The men tested the chain. Once they were satisfied that the girls could not escape, they left, and the huge metal door clanged shut, leaving them alone again.

Outside the building, Kazim turned to his brother, Athir.

"We will not kill them unless we have to, but you must face the fact that if it does not go as planned, we must kill them."

"You promised me, and you're our cell leader."

"I know. I'm sorry, but we have to do it. To protect ourselves, we may have to kill them. The FNP will not tolerate us letting them go if we don't get our people out of prison. I have spoken with them, and they are firm about this. You don't need to be here when we do it. You can stay at home."

"When will you know if you have to kill them?"

"In seventy-two hours."

Athir was dizzy. The world seemed to go dark around him. He leaned against a tree to steady himself.

"It will be all right, little brother. I'll take care of everything, and soon, we will have Fadi back with us again." Kazim patted Athir's shoulder in an attempt to comfort his brother, but instead, Athir felt a chill rise through his spine.

CHAPTER THIRTY-EIGHT

GERHARD AND TOVA were sitting in the Ben Gurion Airport, waiting for the boarding of his plane back to Germany to begin.

"This has been the most wonderful week of my life," Gerhard said. "I thank you for everything, Tova—for everything." He took her hand and gently caressed her palm.

She smiled at him. "I'm glad you came. This was a very special week for me, too."

"My feelings for you run very deep, deeper than I can ever convey to you."

"Yes, I know," she said.

"You don't love me?" he asked.

She shrugged. What was there to say? "I don't know, Gerhard. All I know is I can't go back to Germany with you. But you will come again to Israel next year?"

"Yes, of course. I will return, just as we talked about with the lady at Yad Vashem. I will come every year. This is all I can do to try to right my father's wrongs."

"Again, you are not responsible for your father's actions. You were just a child, Gerhard."

"Yes, well," he said, touching her cheek. "You are very kind, Tova."

She had never felt this way before. Over the past week, she had felt like her empty life was full. She and Gerhard had connected on every level. They talked about everything. He was the first man who had ever really listened when she spoke.

And now he was going home, and she was going home to Aya. Of course, she missed Aya, but wouldn't it be wonderful to have someone to eat with every night instead of just sitting in front of the television in an empty room? And when she was not working, perhaps they would watch a movie together or even just go for a walk or a hike in the mountains. She allowed herself to dream, and now facing reality hurt more than she wanted to admit. Yes, it was a shame that he had to go home. It was more than a shame; it was heartbreaking. But Tova was an Israeli. This was her home, and she would not, could not leave. It was better to be alone in Israel than loved in another country.

The flight attendant began to call the rows, telling the people to come forward and board the plane. Gerhard took Tova into his arms and held her tightly until the last row was called.

"It's time," he said.

"I know." She felt as if someone had carved a hole deep in the pit of her stomach.

"Are you sure you won't come with me?" he asked.

She nodded. "I can't, Gerhard."

"I am going to miss you so much, Tova. I love you," Gerhard said. He squeezed her tightly, kissed the top of her head and lips, and touched her cheek. "I'll keep in touch. I'll write, and I'll call."

She nodded and worked hard to keep the tears from spilling onto her cheeks. He turned and walked toward the boarding ramp. She watched him go. She stared at his back, thinning blond hair and tall, slender frame. She'd come to know this man so well in only a week. A part of her wanted to run to him and say, "Yes, Gerhard, I'll go with you. I'll go with you anywhere. Please don't leave."

He turned once and waved, then gave her a sad smile. He disappeared as he boarded the plane. She watched through the window as the aircraft taxied down the runway. Tova was crying now. Tears were a luxury she almost never allowed herself. But today, she couldn't control her pain. Gerhard was on his way home. He could no longer see her, so she let the tears roll down her cheeks until the plane was airborne and on its way to Germany, carrying the only man she had ever loved.

"God be with you," Tova whispered softly as the aircraft disappeared into the clouds.

"Thank you so much for taking care of Aya," Tova said to her neighbor as she lifted Aya in her carrier.

The cat was meowing repeatedly. Tova knew that Aya was both glad to see her and angry to have been left for so long.

Tova turned the lock and entered her silent apartment. The emptiness seemed even more pronounced now that she'd felt the warmth of sharing her time with another person. She'd never even told Gerhard that she loved him. She couldn't. If she'd even said the words, she was afraid that she would beg him to stay. His life, job, and family were all in Germany. Tova would never live in a country where Hitler had once killed six million of her people. She belonged in Israel. Israel was her home.

The stewardess walked around the cabin, asking if everyone preferred chicken or pot roast. Gerhard couldn't eat. He politely refused. The man sitting beside him was red-faced and obese. He ate the food that was brought to him as if he hadn't eaten in a month. Gerhard tried not to look his way. The gravy from the pot roast was dripping down the man's double chin.

"You should have something to eat," Gerhard's seatmate said. "It's good."

"I'm not hungry. Besides, I've never cared much for airline food."

"This is not too bad. I'm telling you—you should try it."

"Thank you, but not today," Gerhard said. He was sitting next to the window, and the man's hefty frame made him feel boxed in and claustrophobic.

"My name is Wilfred," the man said.

"Gerhard." Gerhard didn't feel like talking. He was trying to sort out so many different feelings inside of him.

"Where are you from?"

"What?" Gerhard was looking out the window.

"Where do you live?" the man asked again.

"Oh, Berlin…"

"I'm from Hamburg."

Gerhard nodded. *Good for you, now please leave me alone.* But, of course, he could not say what he was thinking.

"What do you do for a living?" the man asked, swiping up the last bit of gravy from his plate with the final morsel of bread.

"I'm an engineer. I work on the roadways," Gerhard said.

"Oh, that's very impressive. I work for an import-export company. There are still plenty of Jews in Germany. They want Israeli silver. So, I come here and buy silver."

"That's nice."

"Eh, it's okay. They Jew me down pretty good. You know how they are. Cheap! Between you and me, Hitler had it right."

"Shut up! Shut your mouth!" Gerhard was trembling. Why couldn't he have been seated somewhere else? Preferably beside someone who would respect his need to be left alone.

"Hey, no reason to get upset. I didn't take you for a Jew. You don't look like one…"

"Just stop talking," Gerhard said. Although it came as no surprise, it was a disappointment nonetheless, not only a disappointment but a reminder. Anti-Semitism was alive and well and had not died with the Nazis. Gerhard frowned at his seatmate and then called the flight attendant over.

A pretty girl, who had obviously been chosen for the job because of her attractive girl-next-door appearance, walked up the aisle. Her perfectly styled hair bounced with every step.

"How can I help you, sir?" she asked in perfect German. Then she flashed him a sweet hometown smile.

"I'd like to change seats," Gerhard said.

"Is there a reason, sir? Is something wrong with your seat?"

"Yes, there is a reason," Gerhard said. He was not usually crude or insulting, but this disgusting man had angered him. "This man is quite obviously obese and practically sitting on top of me. I'm very uncomfortable."

"Sir, there's a seat in the back next to the woman with the baby. Nobody wanted to sit there. Are you sure you want to sit by an infant?"

"Yes, that would be fine, preferable, in fact," Gerhard said, and he got up and moved.

The baby woke up and cried on and off for several hours, but the child's mother didn't attempt to talk to Gerhard at all. And for that much, he was thankful. He spent the rest of the trip lost in his thoughts.

CHAPTER THIRTY-NINE

ATHIR NASIR FELT the cool wind against his face as he walked toward the Mosque to say his evening prayers. He loved winter. The weather was so much more agreeable than the summers.

Of course, he understood their plight. He lived it and wanted to see his brother free. But when he thought of the bombings, the murders, and finally, this terrible act of kidnapping, he knew that this was not what he wanted to do with his life.

There was an old man he'd known all his life who was a devout Muslim. His name was Wahib Shadi. He'd befriended Athir after Athir's father died in a fight with Israeli soldiers when Athir was only eight. His mother was overwhelmed raising three boys and hardly had time for anything other than the practical acts of cooking, cleaning, and trying to keep a roof over their heads.

Wahib had become the father he had desperately needed. Wahib was a man of peace. Though a Muslim, he did not believe in jihad and felt that trying to push the Jews out of Israel was an exercise in futility. He was old and wise and had seen the best men of many families killed or imprisoned. He had high hopes for Fadi and Kazim, but only Athir had listened to him.

Kazim was convinced there was no other way to take back the

land stolen from them along the Gaza Strip. He told Athir they must fight to keep Palestine from being overtaken by the Jews.

"They will steal all of our land and everything we have," Kazim told Athir. His brother Fadi agreed, so Athir, the youngest, followed their lead. He'd heard about the blood, the killings, the death, but he'd never seen it. His older brothers had protected him in many ways, and Athir loved them both. He wasn't sure what he felt about the Jews, fear mostly. He'd learned from his brothers not to trust them, and he didn't. But it was certain that murder and kidnapping were not the solutions to this age-old problem.

After he had finished his prayers, Athir went to the market to purchase some oranges and fresh vegetables. Then, he walked for almost a mile to the small dwelling of Wahib Shadi. It was dark, but he could still see the little house beside a dirt road, with a fig tree in the front yard.

Athir knew that tree was Wahib's beloved and most precious possession. Tonight, he felt it extending its branches to welcome him. When Athir was just a boy, that house had seemed like a prosperous home to him. He could still remember how he had helped Wahib gather fruit from the tree, and together, they shared the bounty Allah had given Wahib among all the neighbors.

Now, ten years later, at eighteen, Athir looked at the house with different eyes. He saw the poverty he'd never seen as a child. Wahib appeared rich because he was grateful for everything he had, but was far from a prosperous man. How many wonderful nights Athir had spent wide-eyed and listening to Wahib tell stories of the Prophet and his incredible kindness and wisdom. Those memories were some of the best times in his childhood.

Now that he was becoming a man, he observed the kindness the Prophet taught did not extend toward the kafirs—Jews, Christians, and idolaters. But the way Wahib told the stories, he could believe that kindness was for all men.

Now that Athir was old enough to earn money, he would come once a week and bring food for Wahib. He planned to look after the old man for the rest of Wahib's life. In fact, he'd asked Wahib to move in with him, his mother, and his brother, but Wahib had refused, grateful but unwilling to be a burden.

Athir shuddered. He had to talk to someone, and he trusted Wahib. If Kazim knew what Athir was about to do, he would be terribly angry. It had been made clear to Athir that he must not tell anyone about the kidnapping or where the girls were being kept. But Athir could no longer hold the secrets inside of him. They were eating away at him like a cancer from the inside out. Wahib would know what to do; he would have an answer.

When Athir arrived at Wahib's home, he noticed how badly the paint on the small structure had begun to chip. He wondered why he had not seen it before. But it was no wonder.

Wahib was growing old. He was old when Athir met him, but now he was probably a little over seventy. It was hard for a man that age to keep everything up. Athir made a mental note that as soon as things settled with his brothers, he would come and sand down the old paint and then put a new coat on the little house for Wahib.

Athir's hand trembled as he knocked at the wooden door and waited. On the side of the building was a small stained-glass window. Athir knew this window would catch the last light of day inside the house, and the red glass would sparkle across the dirt floor like rubies. This was the window of Wahib's prayer room. Athir had prayed there many times, and when he did, he'd felt such peace.

Wahib opened the door. He wore a loose-fitting shirt and matching pants that had once been white but had long since yellowed with age and use. His long, gray beard was combed, and on his head, he wore a black and white keffiyeh made of mostly cotton and some wool that hung loosely about his shoulders and was fastened with an agal.

Athir handed the package of foodstuff to Wahib and kissed the old man on both cheeks.

"As-salamu alaykum," Wahib said, smiling broadly. "Thank you for this," he said, indicating the package.

"As-salamu alaykum," Athir answered. "No need for thanks. It's nothing, just a small token."

"Come in, my friend. It is so good to see you. Can I offer you some food, something to drink?"

"No, no, thank you," Athir answered. They spoke to each other in their native Arabic. "I hope you have a few minutes. I need to talk."

"Of course. For you, I always have time." Wahib smiled. "Let's take a walk. It is certainly a beautiful night that Allah has blessed us with. We should enjoy it."

Athir nodded. Wahib walked beside him carrying his Subha, a strand of ninety-nine white prayer beads that he used to glorify God. They strolled down the familiar streets. It was only a short time after ten o'clock, but only a few people were still outside. The stars glittered in the midnight-blue sky. Neither of them spoke for several minutes until they came upon a beggar. Wahib did not say a word, but he took all the change he had in his pocket and put the coins into the man's cup.

"Thank you," Wahib said to the beggar.

Athir smiled. "I remember."

"You remember what?" Wahib said with a smile because he already knew what Athir remembered.

"The story you once told me."

"Oh, I told you many stories. To which one of them are you referring?"

"The one that explains that it is better to give than to receive. That's why you thanked the poor man, isn't it? You thanked him for the opportunity to give."

"Yes, Athir. Exactly right. It is a blessing to be able to give to someone."

Athir smiled into the darkness. He loved this old man. He'd loved him since the day they met. It was strange because Wahib had become close to all three brothers. Yet, Athir was the only one who had allowed Wahib's teachings to influence his way of thinking and his life. Perhaps it was because he was the youngest of the three boys. The firstborn, Kazim, was the oldest and, from the day their father had been killed, had assumed the role of the man of the house. Fadi was two years younger than Kazim, and he followed his older brother blindly. But Athir had come as a surprise to his parents six years after Fadi. He was the baby, and the entire family treated him like a child even as he grew older.

"May I be so bold as to ask how your friend is doing?" Wahib asked.

"What friend?" Athir said, pretending not to understand, but he knew that Wahib was talking about Raeda, the girl Athir was in love with.

"Oh, you know who I mean," Wahib laughed. "The pretty girl who has caught your eye and your heart."

"Raeda? She is fine. I see her sometimes, and I am always overcome by her beauty. I've been saving money so that I can offer her a nice dowry when I ask for her hand in marriage."

"A wife is a gift from Allah. You know this, of course. I have told you many times. Once you are married, you must always remember to treat her well. But before you even consider marriage, you must be able to support her, to provide a home and the things she will need. Our beloved Prophet, peace be with him, made this very clear."

"Yes. I am trying to do everything I can to be a good husband to her and a father to our future children. I am planning to go to school in America. I want to study medicine. I have very good grades and have already been accepted into a medical school in the United States."

"This is a good thing. Have you told Raeda of your plans?"

"I've already told her. I sort of hinted that I would like for her to marry me and go with me. In the beginning, while I am in school, we would be poor, but only in money, not in spirit. In spirit, because of our love, we will always be rich."

"You're right, my son. Real riches come from God, not from money. If you love her, and she loves you, you will always be rich. It would be better if you were established before marriage, but I understand you want her to go with you if you go to America."

Athir sighed. "I would be most blessed if she would be my wife. She is the most beautiful person I have ever known. When I look at her, she takes my breath away. But that is only the smallest thing about her that I love. Mostly, it is her heart that is the most precious thing about her. She is kind and good. I will care for her for the rest of our lives, as our Prophet, peace be with him, has said it should be."

"You are a good son and a good Muslim, Athir. You make me very proud."

Athir trembled slightly, although the air was not chilly. The guilt he felt was swallowing him up like quicksand. He knew that he must tell Wahib why he had come. Once Wahib knew what he had become involved in, would Wahib still be proud of him? Athir dreaded exposing the truth about the two American girls being held in deplorable conditions and his part in the entire plan.

They walked in silence for several minutes. A slight breeze caressed the trees, but the night was still otherwise. The only sound was the honking of a car horn in the distance.

"So, Athir, something is wrong. I can sense this from you. I know you too well not to see that you have come tonight with a heavy heart. What is it? What did you want to talk to me about?" Wahib asked.

"How do you feel about the Jews?"

"The Jews," Wahib said, stroking his beard. "This is why you have come? Hmmm. The Jews will fight to the bitter end to keep their homeland, and the Palestinians will do the same to get it back. The bloodshed will never end."

"There is so much hatred in the world. So much is wrong."

"Yes, and it is destroying everything that Allah has provided for us."

"Wahib. I don't know what to do. I am troubled beyond anything I have ever felt before."

"Go ahead. Tell me, my son, what is on your mind? Speak now. I am listening."

"My brothers," Athir said, "my brothers are members of a

group that is a part of the Fatah. You know this, of course. You are aware that Fadi is in prison."

"Yes, your brothers have lost their way. I had hoped they would not go down that path and live. Sometimes, I think maybe they have been possessed by an evil jinn."

"That could very well be the case because things have gotten way out of hand. I have not told you until now because I didn't want to worry you, but it is worse than it was before. I, too, am now involved."

"But why? Why would you, my precious son, who is wise, become involved with a group of terrorists? Have I not taught you better?"

"Yes, Father, you have, and I am most ashamed of this because you have taught me so well. But I became involved because of my brother, Fadi. Kazim wanted to find a way to free Fadi and some of his other friends. It has all become very twisted and complicated. When Kazim first came to me with his plan, I thought it was a good idea. I only agreed to help because I missed Fadi so much. Now I have made a terrible mistake and don't know what to do."

Wahib waited. He did not say a word. Athir cleared his throat and said, "You see, my brother and the rest of his group took two Jewish girls hostage. These girls are from America, and they are young. I think that they are close to my age. The FPN, which, as you know, is the name of the terrorist group, is holding these two girls prisoner in a dark warehouse.

"Kazim has already made contact with Mossad and the American embassy. He told them that he would trade the girls for Fadi and some other members of Fatah who were in prison. I was willing to cooperate with this plan.

"But earlier today, Kazim told me that if our people are not released, they will have no choice but to kill the girls. Kazim said that if they do not get what they want and they don't kill the girls, the FPN is going to kill them, and I am sick to my heart about it.

"Wahib, I cannot betray my own brother and turn him in to the authorities. There is no doubt they will put him in prison or maybe even execute him. As you can well imagine, my mother suffers enough with Fadi in prison. She cries all the time. And yet, how can I stand by and watch as Kazim murders two young women? I am confused and conflicted. My insides are twisted like a knotted rope. I must do something, but I don't know what to do. You, my dear friend, have been like a father to me and are the wisest man I know. So, I've come to you for advice." Athir took a deep breath and waited for Wahib to answer.

"Where are these girls?"

"Let's walk, I'll show you," Athir said.

They had walked for a half hour before they arrived at their destination.

When they got to the building, Athir said. "They are in there."

"Do you have the key?"

"No, only Kazim has the key."

Wahib nodded, and then he sighed so loudly that the sound carried in the night air. "Come. We will go to my house and have some tea."

Athir sat on the floor next to a low table next to Wahib. Wahib poured the steaming-hot tea into two old and chipped porcelain teacups.

"But Wahib?" Athir asked.

"It will all be all right," Wahib said, putting his arm around Athir. "You be sure to stay far away from the warehouse. Do as I say. Do you understand me?"

"Yes."

"Will you do as I say?"

"Yes."

"Do you have the acceptance papers for that college in America and all your other identification papers?"

"Yes, of course."

"Do you have pictures of yourself and Raeda?" he asked.

"Yes, but why?"

"Bring all of your papers and all of Raeda's papers and pictures to me here in one hour. I will take care of everything. Trust me."

CHAPTER FORTY

ATHIR LEFT as he was bidden, and Wahib watched his back as he disappeared down the noisy, crowded street. Once he was sure that Athir couldn't see him, he grabbed a couple of coins from his coin jar in his cupboard and walked down the street to a payphone. He dropped the coins in the phone coin-slot and dialed the number. The phone rang twice.

"Mossad, Amsel speaking."

"As-salamu alaykum, my friend."

"And shalom, my friend. How are you, Wahib?"

"There is much trouble. I must see you tonight."

"Remember the old safe house where we met in the Arab quarter?"

"Yes."

"We moved to a new one two blocks to the south. There is a palm tree in front of the building. I will leave a light on in the left room from the street, so you can be sure. I will be there in an hour."

"Thank you. Peace be upon you."

"Shalom."

Elan called Mrs. Finkelstein and told her to watch Noa and that he would come home late that evening.

Elan lit the wick on the oil lamp, trimmed it, and placed it in the window of the left room as agreed. He was dressed in an Arab style: a cream-colored dishdasha with a plain, light brown vest, leather sandals, and a green and white keffiyeh headdress wrapped around the head, neck, and lower face. He unwound the headdress and laid it on the kitchen counter. He checked his watch, and it read seven-thirty. The last rays of the setting sun were soon to vanish from his window.

Elan put the teapot on to boil and opened the cupboard for something to offer his guest. Mossad kept the kitchen stocked to help entertain informants and agents who needed to lie low but remain in the Arab quarter. This new safe house was just set up after the last one had been compromised.

Ah, perfect. He reached into the cupboard and found some dates, a bottle of balsamic vinegar, and a bottle of olive oil. There was some fresh pita bread in the fridge, and he turned the oven on to two hundred fifty degrees and let it warm up. He tore two pitas in half and laid them on a stone to put in the oven when his guest arrived. The teapot whistled, and Elan reached over and turned the burner off.

Elan had interrupted his investigation to meet with Wahib. They had an understanding that Mossad never sought Wahib out. Wahib would come to them if he knew anything that would be helpful to Mossad. Elan hoped that the information Wahib wanted to discuss with him tonight was about the girls and would be of help to them.

There was a soft tapping on the door to his apartment. Elan retrieved the silenced 9mm pistol from the holster under his vest, made his way to the door, and stopped, positioning himself at the door's side.

"Who is it?" Elan asked.

"Wahib."

Elan holstered his gun and opened the door. "Shalom, my friend."

"As-salamu alaykum, my friend."

"Come in. The teapot has just come to a boil. The oven is hot. I will pop some pita into it and warm it up."

"Thank you. That is a kind and gracious gesture."

"It is the least I can do. We rarely see each other, and I want to break bread with you as we talk. Please take a seat at the table. Wahib took a position on the floor beside the traditional low table. Elan placed the stone with the pita bread on it into the oven and poured hot water into two teacups with a loose-leaf tea ball in them. He placed the two teacups on saucers and brought them to the table.

"Be right back," he told the older man.

Wahib smiled and nodded.

Elan took two plates out of the cupboard and poured some olive oil on one-half of each plate and balsamic vinegar on the other half. He shook some *za'atar* spice onto the olive oil on each plate. The pita was now warm. He grabbed an oven mitt, opened the oven, and removed the stone.

The smell of the bread filled the room, and he realized he was hungry. He grabbed the two plates and the small bowl of figs he had set aside and placed them on the table. Returning to the stovetop, he grabbed two half-pitas and returned to sit down with Wahib.

Elan waited until Wahib prayed the blessing, and they turned their attention to the meal. They both removed the tea balls and sipped the steaming hot liquid. They tore off pieces of pita and dipped them in the vinegar and then the olive oil and *za'atar* spice. The men ate in silence for a while, and then Elan thought it was time to break the silence.

"Wahib, you said there was trouble. How can I help you?"

Wahib put his teacup down and sighed. "I have some information for you, and I need your help as well."

"What can I do for you, old friend?"

Wahib retrieved an envelope with papers and pictures. He placed the pictures of the two young people on the table.

"These two young people are good people. They deserve a chance to live a good, peaceful life. They will soon be married, and the boy has been accepted into medical school in America. Here is his acceptance letter to medical school."

"How can I help?"

"It has to do with the information. He is a good boy and has been sucked into bad business with his brothers."

"Has this anything to do with the American girls' kidnapping?"

"Yes, exactly. This boy's name is Athir Nasir."

"Is he related to Fadi Nasir, one of the FPN members that the FPN is trying to get released?"

"Yes, he is his brother, but he needs to be free of their influence and start a life of peace, learn to be a doctor, and heal people."

"What is needed?"

"I need a passport for each, two airfares to America, and some money to help them along when they get there. And if he is on a terror watchlist, his name needs to be removed."

Elan exhaled. "That's a lot to ask for."

"It is a bargain. The Americans will help you. The boy showed me where the girls are being held, and I will show you."

"Are you asking me to make a deal?"

The old man smiled. "No, my friend. I will tell you where they are because it is the right thing to do. You will help this boy and his girl because it is also the right thing to do." He handed Elan a piece of paper with the address written on it.

"I will make someone listen and get you what you want."

"May the blessing of Allah be upon you, my friend."

They finished another cup of tea and a few dates, and Wahib excused himself and left.

Elan washed the dishes they had used, put everything away, placed the papers and pictures in a pocket in his vest, and blew out the lamp. He wrapped his head and face back up in his keffiyeh, closed and locked the front door, and headed out into the night. He had to get back to the Mossad office and start calling some people.

CHAPTER FORTY-ONE

THAT NIGHT, Athir was lying on his bed thinking. He assumed that Wahib was planning to talk to Kazim. And as much as he wanted to believe that Kazim would listen to Wahib, he knew that his brother would not heed the advice of an old man. He also knew that Kazim would be angry with him for telling Wahib what the FPN was doing.

Athir was sure that the girls would die, and he would have done nothing to prevent their deaths. How could he ever pray and speak to Allah again without guilt? Another thing bothered him. What did Wahib want with those pictures and papers? He did not sleep well that night.

Wahib had proven to be a genuine intelligence source before, so Mossad trusted him. Elan trusted him, too, but trying to extract hostages from a terrorist lair is always dangerous.

Elan Amsel and five other Mossad agents stormed the warehouse, taking the terrorists by surprise. Only two of the terrorists were present at the time that Mossad arrived: Kazim and another man. Kazim ran to the table, took a gun, and aimed it at Elan. Elan shot both men dead within seconds. He'd always been a perfect shot. The two terrorists lay in a pool of blood across the room from each other. On the table, Elan saw a pile of weapons.

"You stay here," Elan pointed to a tall male Mossad agent. "Make sure you watch the door in case more of them come in. I think the old man was telling the truth, but we still need to be careful. It could still be a setup."

"Yes, sir," the junior officer responded.

Then, with guns extended, the agents carefully plowed through the warehouse, looking for other FPN members who might be hiding. They saw no one. Once Elan was sure that there were no other terrorists in the building, he and the others began to search for the girls.

One of the agents found a locked steel door and yelled for the others. Elan shot the lock off the door and then pulled it open. The sound of metal against metal thundered throughout the building, and Bari's heart pounded like a triphammer. She was not sure what was taking place outside the small room where she and Marilyn huddled together on the floor.

A few minutes earlier, when they'd heard the gunshots, Marilyn had begun to whimper again. Now, there was the sound of the door bursting open. Anything could happen, anything at all.

"There they are," one of the Mossad agents said.

Marilyn was shaking so hard that Bari felt her body trembling in response.

Two female Mossad agents went over, untied, and removed the blindfolds from Bari and Marilyn. Both girls were crying. Their knees were wobbling so hard they could barely stand. Elan walked over and helped them to their feet.

Elan could see a hint of red in Bari's hair and immediately knew she was his daughter in the light that filtered through the darkness. She got her red hair from her mother. Elan had a quick flashback to the first time he saw Janice. He was working at his father's fruit stand in the market, and the first thing he noticed was that fiery hair.

"I am Elan Amsel. I am your father," he said to Bari.

Bari was so overcome with a wild mixture of emotions that all she could do was break down into deep sobs.

When Bari put her hands over her eyes, Elan saw a bit of Noa in the gesture. It was ever so slight, but just the way in which Bari moved made Elan think of his other daughter. He, too, was suddenly overcome with emotion, and he took Bari in his strong, capable arms. She buried her dirty face in his muscular chest and wept.

One of the female Mossad agents was holding Marilyn, for she, too, was crying. "Come, everyone. Let's get out of this place," Elan said.

CHAPTER FORTY-TWO

Noa spent over an hour getting ready for her sister's arrival. She set her hair on electric rollers and then tried on three different dresses, but none of them was to her liking. Finally, she settled on her favorite pair of jeans and a silky white blouse. She came out of her room to show her father how she looked. Elan nodded his approval.

"You are beautiful no matter what you wear, just like your mama was," Elan said, smiling, but his heart broke as he watched his daughter and thought about Nina. Nina, God, how he missed her.

Bari Lynn and Noa greeted each other clumsily at first, but within a half hour, it seemed they had been friends forever. Janice and Elan spoke. It was mostly small talk, very little reminiscing, but at least they had found peace with each other. Elan did not understand how Lucas could sit so quietly and say nothing.

Lucas hardly spoke, and it seemed to Elan that no matter what Janice said, Lucas never argued with his wife over anything. Yet somehow, Elan did not see this man as weak. There was an inner strength in Lucas that Elan could not figure out. And even though they were very different, Elan liked Lucas. It was hard not to like him.

By the end of the day, Elan was glad he'd brought them all

together. It was good for Noa and Bari. But it was also good for him and Janice to settle their problems from so long ago finally. Bari was his child, and he could sometimes see himself when he looked at her. But she seemed much more like Lucas, the man who had raised her.

Elan thought he should still be angry because she kept him in the dark all these years about Bari's existence. However, he wasn't. He was, in fact, grateful to Lucas for having been a good father to Bari. If Elan had known about Bari when she was born, he wondered if he would have been as good a father. He was young at the time, still restless and wild. Perhaps it had all worked out for the best.

CHAPTER FORTY-THREE

Kazim had never had the opportunity to recite the Shahada with a holy person when he was dying. Athir prayed that his brother had said it alone in his mind as he left the world. It was hard for Athir not to blame himself for everything that had happened. His mother cried constantly. Two of her sons had now gone away from her. One forever, the other for a long time. Kazim was dead, and Fadi was in prison.

Only Athir was left to her, and he had just received a letter saying he had been accepted to the University of Wisconsin in America. Now, his dream of going to America was crushed. Being the brother of a terrorist in prison and one who was just killed in a political kidnapping put him on the terrorist watchlist. He had no hope of being allowed into America.

That night, Athir tenderly wrapped Kazim's body in the traditional three pieces of white fabric. The first, he lovingly pulled over his brother's head like a shirt. The second he used to cover the bottom of Kazim's body.

As he wrapped the third completely over the entire corpse, he began to weep. Long, heartfelt sobs bubbled up like a volcano from the artery in Athir's heart. He loved Kazim, and in many ways, he could not help regretting what he had done. If he had never told Wahib, would Kazim still be alive? Or would Kazim and Athir both be dead and the girls, too?

There was no way to tell what would have happened. The situation had gotten so out of control. Still, for the rest of his life, Athir knew that he would carry the guilt of the death of his brother on his shoulders, and it would always remain buried deep within his heart.

Only the family was present as Kazim's wrapped body was laid on the ground. The heart-wrenching cries of his mother could be heard echoing across the burial ground. How could the sun shine so brightly and the leaves of the trees glisten in such stunning shades of green even while Athir felt such pain? These thoughts ran like a ticker tape inside of his head.

Late that afternoon, when the funeral ended, Athir went to Wahib's house to see Wahib.

They sat outside on the concrete stoop. Neither of them spoke. Athir moved some stones that were lying on the ground with a stick he found that had fallen from the nearby tree.

"I can't believe that my brother is dead. He is gone forever from this life. I will never see him again." Athir bit his lower lip. He knew it was Wahib and should be angry with Wahib, but he wasn't. He knew that Wahib only did what must be done.

"I know. I am sorry for you and your mother."

"After all of this, I will not be permitted to go to America," Athir said, with downcast eyes and heart.

Wahib withdrew an envelope from his robe. "Inside this are your passports and two airplane tickets to America, one-way, of course."

"The Americans will never let me onto their soil. I am a brother to two known terrorists."

"It is arranged. You are not regarded as a threat to anyone. You will be able to stay in America as long as you want, even to become a citizen if you wish."

"How?"

"It is the will of Allah. You will be a man of peace and make me and your mother proud."

"I don't think I can go to America and leave my mother."

"Perhaps you should take her with you? I can get another passport and ticket."

"She would never go. This is her home. Her sisters are here. She is too attached to this place. But I can't help it. I want to get away from here, Wahib. As long as I stay, the Fatah will want me to be a part of them. I can't do that."

"Yes, you're right. Then you must go to America. Take the woman you love, marry her, and leave this place. Try to convince your mother to go with you. But if she refuses, you must go anyway."

Athir felt his throat tighten. He knew what Wahib advised was the right path for him, but he had never been further than fifty miles from where he was born. It would take courage to build a new life in a new land. But he would go forward and take the leap of faith. He would put his trust in Allah.

"You told them, didn't you? You went to Mossad and told them everything," Athir said. He was looking down at the ground, watching a group of ants walking in a line on their way to an unknown destination.

"Yes." Wahib took a long breath. "It was me. I told them."

Athir nodded.

"I'm sorry. I never wanted to do this to you and to your family. Believe me. It was not something I would have chosen to do if I had any other choice."

Athir nodded again. "I know that. You loved Kazim, too." There were tears in his eyes.

"I did love him. I loved all three of you boys like you were my own sons. But fighting against Israel is futile and will only result in endless cycles of death and loss. You were made by Allah for something better. Fulfill your destiny."

"I will," Athir said.

Wahib put his arm around Athir, and Athir wept as the old man held him like a son. At some point, the day had turned to night, but still, they sat together in silence.

When Abdul and two other close friends and members of the FPN arrived, Wahib and Athir were still outside.

Athir looked at Wahib in fear. Wahib nodded.

"I have been expecting you," Wahib said to the young men who looked like hoodlums.

"You betrayed your own brother?" Abdul said to Athir, ignoring Wahib. "We know it was you. We know because you were the only one who knew where the girls were being held, and it was more than obvious to us that you were against the mission from the start. You should be ashamed of yourself. Kazim was your blood. He loved you, Athir. All your brother ever wanted was to see Palestine free for your children and for mine and to free your brother Fadi. Was that such a terrible thing? Was it, Athir?"

Athir stood. His eyes met Abdul's. "I did what had to be done. You know that what you are doing is wrong. You were going to kill two young, innocent girls."

"He was your brother, Athir! Your own blood, Athir! You care more for two strange girls than for your brother? What kind of man are you?"

Abdul pulled a gun out of his pants pocket. "I should let you live so you can live with the guilt of what you did for the rest of your life. But I can't because I can't trust you. You are the enemy now."

Wahib got to his feet. He was slight of build and a little hunched, but he stood tall to meet Abdul's eyes. "It was not Athir who betrayed you. It was me."

"You, old man? You? How could you know where we were holding the girls if Athir didn't tell you?" Abdul's hand that held the gun was trembling.

"Kazim told me. You forget I was like a father to him, too. He trusted me."

"Kazim? Kazim told you, and you betrayed him? How could you? Why would you?"

"Because, as you should know, I am a man of peace. I am a religious man, and terrorism is against everything I believe in. If you must kill someone, kill me, not Athir. He is not responsible."

"But," Athir said. "It was not Wahib…"

"It was me," Wahib said convincingly. "Don't try to protect me, Athir. I will take responsibility for what I have done. I have done what I have done because it is not right to kidnap innocent young girls. I betrayed you. I am not a terrorist; I am a man of peace."

"Who is protecting who?" Abdul said aloud.

"Please, don't hurt him. I promise you, I am the one who told the authorities where you were keeping the girls," Athir pleaded.

"It is not the first time I have opposed the FPN. I told the Mossad about Fadi and his partners that did the bombing of the medical clinic," the old man confessed.

"No, it's not true!" Athir said.

"Stop trying to protect the old man, Athir. He betrayed you and your brothers—both of your brothers," Abdul said, and then he shot Wahib. "Stupid old man," Abdul said. "Come on, let's go. Let's get out of here." Abdul nodded his head to the other members of the FPN, and they took off into the night.

Wahib fell so softly to the ground that it was as if his soul had already begun transcending. Athir bent down beside his old friend, and with his voice filled with pain, he began to recite the words of the Shahada. Wahib's eyes were closed. Had he heard?

Athir held his breath as he waited for a sign. Then, as was customary for a devout Muslim when he was dying, Wahib raised his index finger to let Athir know that he'd heard the words of the Shahada. He'd spoken them into his heart as he left the earth to meet his beloved Allah.

"I know you did what you had to do. I forgive you, Wahib," Athir whispered softly and wept as one would weep for his father.

CHAPTER FORTY-FOUR

ATHIR NEVER TOLD his mother that Wahib was responsible for
Kazim's death and Fadi's imprisonment. She understood that he
loved Wahib like a father. Athir performed the service of preparing
his body for burial, as he had done for Kazim.

The pain was deeper than it was for Kazim. He had drawn the
old man into this mess, and he died because of it. Athir spent the
time of mourning that was customary for a father, though techni-
cally, he and Wahib were not related.

When the days of mourning were over, Athir approached
Raeda's father for permission to marry her. Wahib had left Athir his
house, and Raeda's father accepted it as a dowry. He was especially
pleased to see the plane ticket, passports, and acceptance letter to
the medical school in America.

The El Al flight from Tel Aviv to Chicago O'Hare landed on the
tarmac and rolled to a stop. Athir and Raeda would catch their
connecting flight to Milwaukee, then take a bus to Madison,
Wisconsin, where they would settle in before registering at the
University Of Wisconsin School Of Medicine.

Mossad had convinced Washington that they would pay for the
plane tickets, but Washington had to foot the bill for a full-ride

scholarship and a stipend to support the young couple through medical school. The U.S. considered it a bargain. Good intel was worth its weight in gold, and the young man had proven his loyalty.

The ground crew rolled out the stairs to the aircraft. After the stewardess thanked them for flying El Al Air, the passengers got up and started getting out their suitcases from the overhead bin. The Mossad agent on the *proof of life* call has personally bought the couple a set of suitcases for their trip. The couple dressed in American-style clothing. He wore a black pair of slacks, a white shirt, and a black pair of shoes. She wore a very conservative green dress, a gold scarf, and a pair of black leather pumps. Athir insisted that if they were to live in America, they would dress like Americans, albeit like the conservative ones. Raeda already liked America and decided that she would go shoe shopping when they could afford it.

The couple rolled their new wheeled suitcases to customs and got in line. The busyness of the place was almost dizzying to the couple. Finally, it was Athir's turn at the custom window. He handed his passport to the blonde customs agent, who smiled at him.

"Sir, do you have anything to declare?"

Athir contemplated the question for a moment. "Yes. I am so grateful that you invited me to America!" he said with a broad grin.

The agent smiled and stamped his passport.

CHAPTER FORTY-FIVE

TOVA LOOKED in the small mirror in the compact she kept in her purse. She fluffed up her hair for the one-hundredth time today. Gerhard's flight would be arriving in less than fifteen minutes. It had been a year since she'd seen him, but he'd called her consistently every week, and they'd talked long distance for an hour. She hated to think of his phone bill.

But over the year, she'd realized how much she missed him, and although they'd only spent one week together, it was the happiest week of her life. He told her he loved her every time they spoke, and although her heart melted like butter at the sound of those words, it was hard for her to say them back to him. She finally told him she loved him, but she could not say it as often as he said it to her.

She'd spent quite a bit of money preparing her apartment for Gerhard's arrival. Aya had already gotten fur on the new bed sheets and the new sofa that Tova had purchased. But all in all, Tova was satisfied with the way everything looked.

This visit would be the first time that Gerhard would speak at Yad Vashem. They were going to Jerusalem for three days. Aya was staying with Tova's neighbor. It was all arranged. During their phone conversations, Gerhard had told Tova how nervous he was about public speaking but how honored he felt to be allowed to make this small gesture of apology for his father's behavior.

Tova fidgeted as she looked up at the screen above her. Gerhard's plane had just landed. In less than ten minutes, he would be here beside her. She leaned against the post and waited, short of breath and nervous.

Gerhard's heart was thumping. His stomach was alive with excitement. He and Tova, what an unlikely pair they made. How perfect it was, all in God's plan. Gerhard followed the crowd out of the airplane. Then, when he saw Tova standing across the aisle in the airport, it was all he could do not to run to her. She was even more beautiful than he remembered.

"Gerhard," Tova called out.

Now Gerhard could not help but run. It seemed like miles until he reached her. When he got there, Gerhard took Tova into his arms. She let out a small laugh, and then they kissed.

In his eyes, she was a beautiful young girl. In her eyes, he was a handsome prince. In reality, they were two lonely middle-aged people. She was a little overweight with a plain face, and he was slender but without any muscle and balding. It was strange how they had met, how, with their bloodlines, they should have been enemies. But instead, God had made them twin souls.

"Tova, I am thinking that maybe I can get a job here."

"In Israel?"

"They need engineers in Israel, don't they? I have a good resume."

"Really?" she asked. "You mean it? Of course, they need engineers in Israel."

"I want to marry you. You will never leave this country. I know how you feel about Israel. So, I decided that I would come to you. Besides, if I live here, I will be available more than once a year to go to speak at Yad Vashem if they will have me."

She cocked her head and looked at him in disbelief. "You would give up your job? Your home?"

"Yes, for you, I would. I want to be happy, Tova. I am no longer young. I want to spend the years I have left with you. What is life without happiness?"

Her eyes were shining as she looked up at him. "You are serious?"

"Very. So, what's your answer?"

"My answer? What's your question?"

He set his suitcase down on the ground. Then, Gerhard got down on one knee. People at the airport stopped to watch as Gerhard took a small box out of his pocket.

"Tova Ben-Levi, will you please be my wife?"

Tova felt her knees go weak. Life was so strange. God was so miraculous. Only a year ago, she'd gone to work, and her boss had told her she was to interrogate a Nazi for kidnapping two Jewish teenagers. Then she not only found out that he was not a Nazi, but a good man, and now she was about to accept his proposal of marriage. It was so strange how one could turn a corner; when they least expected it, their lives could change forever.

"Yes! Yes, Gerhard. Yes, I will marry you."

The crowd of people who'd gathered around the two of them began to clap. Gerhard slipped the ring on Tova's finger. Then, he stood up and took her into his arms. This, too, was Israel.

CHAPTER FORTY-SIX

KATJA RECOGNIZED Noa Amsel when she walked into the rehearsal. There was to be a talent show that featured all the best talents from the local schools. Everyone who was prominent in society would be attending because the cost of tickets was to be donated to the organization for The Wives of Fallen Israeli Soldiers. This was the last year that Katja would be president of the organization. She and John wanted to travel, and she'd finally decided that she'd devoted enough of her life to charity. It was her turn to enjoy life.

After Zofia passed quietly in her sleep six months prior, Katja had felt a terrible loss. She leaned heavily on her husband for support. That was when John suggested that they take some time to relax. He'd suggested that they go somewhere exotic, like Australia. Money was not an issue. He had a good job, with plenty of vacation time available, and she had made good investments with the money that Mendel had left her.

Katja had spent most of her life in retribution for the thoughts that had possessed her mind the night before Mendel went to war. It was not until she explained all of her feelings to John that Katja could finally release the guilt. For years, she'd carried that remorse like a weight that bore down on her, keeping her head below the surface of life.

As she and John had predicted, interracial marriage had plenty of challenges. Many times, they went into a restaurant, and others turned and stared. People who Katja had believed were friends turned their backs on her when she married John. She and John were not invited to lots of parties, and that hurt Katja. But the love and support they shared outweighed the pain of being ostracized.

"Good morning, Mrs. Russell," Noa said as she came bouncing through the back door of the auditorium, carrying her pink plastic duffel bag that held her ballet shoes, costume, and a towel.

"Good morning, Noa."

"You remembered my name? After a whole year? You still remembered me," Noa said, smiling.

She was such a pretty child, Katja thought. "But of course. You remembered my name, didn't you?"

"Everyone knows who you are, Mrs. Russell. You're a very important lady."

Katja laughed. "I don't know about all of that. But it is good to see you again, Noa."

"Thank you. I'm glad to be here. I was so nervous during the audition. I still can't believe I was selected."

"Well, we are glad to have you. You are an excellent dancer."

"I want to go into the theater when I get older," Noa said. "I would love to be in musicals."

"I believe that you can do whatever you set your mind to doing." Katja smiled.

She watched Noa climb the stairs to the dressing rooms. *She looked a little like Elan, but her mother must have been beautiful.* Suddenly, Katja felt that old stab of pain, the pain of the past, the pain of the love she and Elan had once shared so long ago.

How different she'd thought her life was going to be when she and Elan were engaged. A bittersweet smile crept over her lips. It was sad that things had turned out the way that they did.

She'd loved Elan. But then again, if she and Elan had married, she would never have given birth to Ima, her wonderful daughter who had just told her last week that she was going to have a baby. Katja smiled. She was going to be a grandmother. If she had married Elan, she would never have known Mendel's tender devotion and thereby built an organization that had been the saving grace for many widows.

But most of all, if she and Elan had married, she would never have known the joy of reciprocal love. Reciprocal love—the love she shared with John, her best friend, her confidant, her true beshert. John was the man who taught her that God did not see color or bloodlines. God saw only love.

CHAPTER FORTY-SEVEN

LATER THAT NIGHT, Elan was sitting in his favorite easy chair. Noa came out of the shower wearing a pink terry-cloth robe with her hair wrapped in a matching towel. She was giddy with excitement. Elan smiled. He knew that Noa was always filled with exuberance after a performance. He'd been at the show, sitting in the back row alone and watching his daughter as she danced the ballet. How lovely she was and how much she looked like her mother.

"Did you like the show, Daddy? Did I do okay?"

"Of course, you know I loved it. And yes, you were excellent, a true prima ballerina. I'm so proud of you."

"Oh, Daddy. Of course, you would say that you always say that." She laughed.

"To me, you are a princess, a beautiful princess." He smiled.

"That's because you're my dad. I called Bari and told her about the show. She was really excited for me."

"You like having a sister, huh?"

"Yeah, I do, even if she is in America. Maybe someday I'll go to America and see her, or she'll come back here again."

Elan smiled and nodded. Noa was just a child. Why burst her bubble? There was no reason to tell her that he doubted Janice or anyone from Janice's family would ever set foot in Israel again. But it was okay. At least he and Janice were on good terms now. The past was finally behind them. Noa had a sister, and he had a daughter, even if she lived in America.

"Is all of your homework done?"

"Not yet. I just have a few things left to do."

"Okay. You finish your homework and then get right off to bed. You have school in the morning," Elan said.

"Yes, Daddy." Noa kissed Elan's cheek. "Sleep well."

Elan nodded.

Elan's heart swelled with pride and a little pain as he watched Noa enter her room. Soon, she would grow up and leave him, first for college, then for her husband.

Elan took a long breath and opened the sliding glass door. He walked outside and sat down on one of the wicker chairs on the patio. Then he took a cigar out of his pocket. After he struck a match and lit the thick body, he puffed. Smoking cigars was something new he'd come to enjoy. *A bad habit*, he thought, but he didn't do it too often.

The sun was setting, painting the sky in shades of fuchsia, orange, and purple. Elan closed his eyes for a moment. Then, in a soft voice, he whispered. "Nina…" How he wished that she were here beside him.

When he opened his eyes and gazed at the land surrounding him, he was once again struck by his love for this country, his love for Israel. Nina had shared that love with him.

"Oh, Nina, if only you could be here. If only you could see how big Noa has gotten. She is a wonderful dancer and almost as beautiful as you."

Of course, he was alone, speaking only into the stillness of the coming night.

Elan Amsel had sacrificed much for the love of his country. He'd given up his first girl, gone to war, and had come close to death more times than he could count. And yet, he would not have his life any other way. He was an Israeli.

The darkness was fast approaching as the full moon made her royal entrance, and the stars became visible in the sky.

In the distance, Elan saw a shooting star and wondered if perhaps it was Nina's way of telling him that she was with him. *How sentimental I have become as I am aging. You're getting soft, Amsel.* He thought as he took another puff.

Yes, he was becoming soft, and every year, he was growing older. His was a lonely life. He had no wife, and he knew that one day, sooner than he wished, Noa would marry and leave him behind. But there was nowhere else on earth that he would rather live out the remaining years of his life, nowhere else he would rather see Noa grow into a woman. There was no other land he would wish for his grandchildren to build the future of Judaism. This was Israel —this was forever his homeland.

The End

AUTHORS NOTE

I always enjoy hearing from my readers, and your thoughts about my work are very important to me. If you enjoyed my novel, please consider telling your friends and posting a short review on Amazon. Word of mouth is an author's best friend.

Also, it would be my honor to have you join my mailing list. As my gift to you for joining, you will receive 3 **free** short stories and my USA Today award-winning novella complimentary in your email! To sign up, just go to my website at www.RobertaKagan.com

I send blessings to each and every one of you,

Roberta

Email: roberta@robertakagan.com

ACKNOWLEDGMENTS

This is the last book in the "All My Love, Detrick" series. It is hard for me to say goodbye to all the characters in these books who have become my old friends. I received several emails requesting I write Dorothy's story (Leah's friend, who went to America in Book One). I have written a novella called "Little Songbird," it's Dorothy's story. If you would like to receive a free digital copy, please go to my website and sign up for my mailing list. My gift to you for joining my wonderful reader family is not only a copy of "Little Songbird" but also another short story called "A Nazi on Trial in God's Court" as well as an award-winning novella titled "Bubbe's Nightengale." I sincerely hope you enjoy them. I send them to you with love.

I also want to thank my daughter and my husband. My husband was very sick when I was finishing this book. However, even though he needed my help in many ways, he always understood that I had to make time for my work. My daughter, as always, is my best friend and my rock. She took care of her father so that I was able to work. I could never have finished this book without her constant assistance.

Once again, and most of all, I want to thank you, the readers. You are the reason that I, with pleasure, devote endless hours to researching and writing. It is my greatest desire that my work pleases you. Thank you for letting me into your life by spending precious time reading my books. It is truly an honor.

ABOUT THE AUTHOR

I wanted to take a moment to introduce myself. My name is Roberta, and I am an author of Historical Fiction, mainly based on World War 2 and the Holocaust. While I never discount the horrors of the Holocaust and the Nazis, my novels are constantly inspired by love, kindness, and the small special moments that make life worth living.

I always knew I wanted to reach people through art when I was younger. I just always thought I would be an actress. That dream died in my late 20's, after many attempts and failures. For the next several years, I tried so many different professions. I worked as a hairstylist and a wedding coordinator, amongst many other jobs. But I was never satisfied. Finally, in my 50's, I worked for a hospital on the PBX board. Every day I would drive to work, I would dread clocking in. I would count the hours until I clocked out. And, the next day, I would do it all over again. I couldn't see a way out, but I prayed, and I prayed, and then I prayed some more. Until one morning at 4 am, I woke up with a voice in my head, and you might know that voice as Detrick. He told me to write his story, and together we sat at the computer; we wrote the novel that is now known as All My Love, Detrick. I now have over 30 books published, and I have had the honor of being a USA Today Best-Selling Author. I have met such incredible people in this industry, and I am so blessed to be meeting you.

I tell this story a lot. And a lot of people think I am crazy, but it is true. I always found solace in books growing up but didn't start writing until I was in my late 50s. I try to tell this story to as many people as possible to inspire them. No matter where you are in your life, remember there is always a flicker of light no matter how dark it seems.

I send you many blessings, and I hope you enjoy my novels. They are all written with love.

Roberta

MORE BOOKS BY ROBERTA KAGAN

AVAILABLE ON AMAZON

Margot's Secret Series

The Secret They Hid

An Innocent Child

Margot's Secret

The Blood Sisters Series

The Pact

My Sister's Betrayal

When Forever Ends

The Auschwitz Twins Series

The Children's Dream

Mengele's Apprentice

The Auschwitz Twins

Jews, The Third Reich, and a Web of Secrets

My Son's Secret

The Stolen Child

A Web of Secrets

A Jewish Family Saga

Not In America

They Never Saw It Coming

When The Dust Settled

The Syndrome That Saved Us

A Holocaust Story Series

The Smallest Crack

The Darkest Canyon

Millions Of Pebbles

Sarah and Solomon

All My Love, Detrick Series

All My Love, Detrick

You Are My Sunshine

The Promised Land

To Be An Israeli

Forever My Homeland

Michal's Destiny Series

Michal's Destiny

A Family Shattered

Watch Over My Child

Another Breath, Another Sunrise

Eidel's Story Series

And . . . Who Is The Real Mother?

Secrets Revealed

New Life, New Land

Another Generation

The Wrath of Eden Series

The Wrath Of Eden

The Angels Song

Made in the USA
Middletown, DE
28 February 2024

50327256R00146